DEADLINES
DON'T CARE
IF JANET
DOESN'T
LIKE HER
PHOTO

ISBN 978-1-7353286-2-1
Deadlines Don't Care If Janet Doesn't Like Her Photo
Revised Edition

www.27bslash6.com

By the same author:

The Internet is a Playground
A *New York Times* bestselling book about overdue accounts, missing cats, and pie charts.

Look Evelyn, Duck Dynasty Wiper Blades, We Should Get Them
A book about design agencies, above ground pools, and magic tea.

That's Not How You Wash a Squirrel
A book about toasted sandwiches, sociopathy, and secret underground tunnels.

Wrap It In a Bit of Cheese Like You're Tricking the Dog
A book about suggestion boxes, buttons, and third-degree burns.

Walk It Off, Princess
A book about cantilevers, secret spots, and Antarctic expeditions.

Deadlines Don't Care if Janet Doesn't Like Her Photo
A book about fish people, office romance, and big red rocks.

Let's Eat Grandma's Pills
A travel book about frogs, buckets, and transparent bubble pods.

For Seb, Holly, and big red rocks.

Puzzle Page

Can you help Ben locate
his Progeria medicine
before his bones turn
to chalk?

Alternate Titles for this Book

Did You Check It For Baby Crabs?

Mr Lovells History of Oral Hygiene

Oh Lordy, It's a Fireball!

I Saw It On a Show About Geishas

I Sent You the Logo in Word Format

What Do You Actually Do All Day?

It Stuck to My Sheets

Big Red Rocks

Who Ate My Panera Salad?

Throwing Soup at Buses

Throwing Seb at Angry Chickens

Magnesium Permanganate

I'm Just the Secretary

Fish People

Contents

JANUARY

S	M	T	W	T	F	S
					1 New years day	2
3	4 Staff regroup?	5	6	7 Snowflake parade	8 Staff regroup? Best Buy	9
10 Post job vacancy	11	12 Zoom meeting	13	14 Ben's puzzle pickup	15 Lunch with Mike	16
17	18	19	20	21	22	23
24 Hire Josh	25	26 no	27	28 Client meeting	29 Fire Josh	30
31						

FEBRUARY

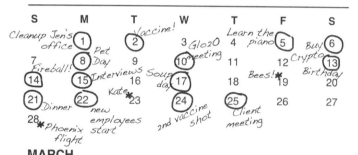

S	M	T	W	T	F	S
Cleanup Jen's office	1	2 Vaccine!	3 Glo2O meeting	4 Learn the piano	5	6 Buy
7 Fireball!	8 Pet Day	9	10	11	12 Crypto	13
14	15 Interviews	16 Soup day	17	18 Bees!	19 Birthday	20
21 Dinner	22	23 Kate	24 2nd vaccine shot	25 Client meeting	26	27
28 Phoenix flight	new employees start					

MARCH

S	M	T	W	T	F	S
Glo2O presentation	1	2 Sedona	3	4 Sharpie my hat	5 Melissa's wedding	6
7	8	9	10	11	12	13
14	15	16	17	18	19	20
21	22	23	24	25	26	27
28	29	30	31			

Foreword

From: David Thorne
Date: Wednesday 27 October 2021 10.04am
To: All Staff
Subject: Book Foreword

Good morning,

As most of you are aware, I usually take my annual leave around this time of year to write. My print deadline is November 16th.

In the past, my books have mostly been a collection of random stories and email correspondences. At the beginning of this year, however, I decided to save myself the stress of coming up with 200+ pages a week before the deadline by writing a page or so every day. As a result, the format of this year's book reads more like a journal and contains a lot of work-related material.

Subsequently, staff names are mentioned throughout, but there's very little background regarding your roles within the agency.

As such, instead of including a foreword that nobody reads, I thought it may be helpful to the reader if everyone here provides a paragraph about how wonderful I am and what a privilege it is to work with me.

To help with your contribution, a couple of key points to consider are:

1. My ability to get along well with everyone.

2. My commitment to creating a healthy work environment.

3. My charm, great hair, and wit.

5. Otters.

If you could have this to me by the end of the week, it would be much appreciated.

This excludes Jason of course, as he's not mentioned in the book.

Thank you, David

....

From: Walter Bowers
Date: Wednesday 27 October 2021 10.17am
To: David Thorne
Subject: Re: Book Foreword

Hello my name is Walter and I work with David and 4 years. David gets along well with everyone and he is committed to creating a healthy work envirmnment. He is charming and he has great hair and he writes funny books.

Is the book about otters? I like otters.

Walter

From: Rebecca Williams
Date: Wednesday 27 October 2021 10.23am
To: David Thorne
Subject: Re: Book Foreword

David,

I'm happy to write something for you but I won't be able to look at it before the end of the week. I'm fully booked today and I have 2 calls scheduled for Thursday morning, a meeting that afternoon, and 3 meetings on Friday.

Checking my schedule for next week, I have Thursday afternoon between 1pm and 4pm free. I might be able to look at it then if that's not too late. I'll pencil it in.

Rebecca

....

From: Gary Wright
Date: Wednesday 27 October 2021 10.30am
To: David Thorne
Subject: Re: Book Foreword

You're not wonderful and I don't appreciate being lied to. Ben told me it was you who has been putting leaves on my desk. I straight up asked you and you lied to my face and said it was probably the wind. Stay out of my office.

Gary

From: Kate Routledge
Date: Wednesday 27 October 2021 10.46am
To: David Thorne
Subject: Re: Book Foreword

Good Morning David,

As HR Director, I'm probably not the best person to ask. Gary has filed 3 formal complaints against you in as many months and Ben filed one last week after you emailed the screenshot of his browser history to all staff.

Please don't put leaves on Gary's desk. It's pointless and upsets him.

Perhaps if you put as much energy into fostering a professional workplace culture as you do into creating chaos, this might be the healthy work environment you claim you're committed to.

Kate

....

From: Jodie Smythe
Date: Wednesday 27 October 2021 10.47am
To: David Thorne
Subject: Re: Book Foreword

No thanks. Why would I do you any favors when you wrote that I have herpes and fucked the rep from Smuckers?

Jodie

From: Ashley Hilditch
Date: Wednesday 27 October 2021 10.48am
To: David Thorne
Subject: Re: Book Foreword

Hello David,

I've learned a lot about identity design in the last six months but I don't know if I can honestly say you're committed to creating a healthy work environment or you get along well with everyone. You ate Melissa's Panera salad yesterday then put the empty container on Jodie's desk and told Melissa she ate it.

Ashley

....

From: Ben Townsend
Date: Wednesday 27 October 2021 10.53am
To: David Thorne
Subject: Re: Book Foreword

Your ability to get along well with everyone? You have a distorted view of reality if you really believe that's true. The only time you get along well with everyone is when you stay home. I can list 3 times just this week that you've instigated an argument for no reason.

1. You told Walter that I had a dream about Ashley giving me a massage. It was a dream about her moving her desk into Gary's office.

2. You told Gary there's a new office policy about wrinkles and he has to get Botox.

3. You taped a piece of cheese under my desk.

You owe me $125 for a pair of new jeans. The cheese left an oil mark on my thigh that doesn't wash out. They're your jeans now. I'm sending you a PayPal request.

Ben

....

From: Mike Campbell
Date: Wednesday 27 October 2021 11.04am
To: David Thorne
Subject: Re: Book Foreword

David,

Sure, I'll drop everything I have on my plate at the moment and write a paragraph about how wonderful you are instead.

I'll get started straight away, I just have to email the regional marketing director of Krispy Kreme and explain that I won't have time to send her a proposal this afternoon because I have to write a story about David's hair.

Honestly, I'm *this close* to just firing everyone and moving to Mexico. What's Melissa's issue today? Is she still sulking about not being allowed to wear fluffy slippers at work? This isn't a retirement home.

I'm going to work from home for the rest of the day. You should come over and see what Patrick has done to the living room. He painted it a pinkish apricot and it's like being inside a giant lung.

Mike

....

From: Melissa Woodcock
Date: Wednesday 27 October 2021 11.05am
To: David Thorne
Subject: Re: Book Foreword

David,

Sorry, I'm not a writer. I'm just the secretary. I'm not allowed to have a personality or an opinion.

It's funny how everyone is allowed to do whatever they want around here except me.

Mel

JAN 2021
1
FRIDAY

I'm not sure what my New Year's resolution is this year. You're meant to have one apparently; it shows you're aware of your failings and know the steps required to be a better person. A thinner person, or a richer one, or maybe kinder. My resolution last year was to clean out the kitchen junk drawer; which doesn't display any self-awareness at all. Or maybe I just chose that at the time because it's easier, safer, to be facetious than to acknowledge your failings to others - to risk having them think, "He's right, he is chonky, broke and mean. Why am I associated with this broken human?"

I never did clean out the junk drawer. Maybe that can be this year's resolution.

I've had better New Year's Eves. Most years, the village we live in has a fireworks show. The fireworks aren't overly impressive - most of the village budget is reserved for the Christmas light pole toppers on main street - but it gives the locals something to do other than watching *Fox News* and polishing their tractors.

"Headin' to the fireworks tonight, Cletus?"

"Wouldn't miss it. Yourself?"

"Lookin' forward to it. I hear they have five this year. Could just be a rumour though."

"Five? Oh Lordy. We're in for a treat. What time are they setting them off?"

"Between 7pm and 7.03pm."

A few years back, after a speed camera was installed on the village traffic light and revenues tripled, the village mayor, Barry, decided to double the size of the fireworks. Barry's assistant lost three fingers and a barn caught fire so it was toned back down after that. Barry actually got in a bit of trouble over the whole thing and there were demands for his resignation. Mainly from the guy who owned the barn. Fireworks are illegal in Virginia, you can't even buy sparklers, so Barry drove over the border into West Virginia to procure them. Apparently, you're also meant to have some kind of license. And insurance.

Barry works at Mattress Firm now. The guy who lost three fingers works at Home Depot in the appliance department. He used to work in the lumber area but lost another finger on the big saw.

The new village mayor, Deanna, is a black woman - which is rather progressive for a community with more Confederate flags than high school diplomas. I once heard a woman at the local supermarket state, "I didn't know negroes eat fish!"

I'm not sure what it was in reference to but it struck me as odd at the time. She was riding one of those store scooters with the orange flags.

Deanna cancelled this year's fireworks due to the pandemic. There was a bit of a protest - the only other free family entertainment in the village is Rape Park or the playable Xbox in a Perspex box at Walmart - but two rednecks holding an illegible sign on Main Street isn't exactly Hands Across America.

"I'm not sure if you've noticed, Deanna, but there's a protest outside."

"There is? Where?"

"Next to the village traffic light."

"The old man and woman sitting in camping chairs?"

"Yes. They have a sign."

"They do? What does it say?"

"I'm not sure, the message appears to be written in thin blue pen on a piece of A4 paper."

"Well that's not very effective. You'd need to stop your car, get out, and walk over to them to read it. They should have used a thick Sharpie."

"Yes. Also, when people drive past, they wave the sign - I suppose in an attempt to gain attention - which makes it even harder to read."

"Do you think there's any correlation between this kind of behaviour and the recent water quality test results?"

"Well, I'm no scientist but 15% lead does seem high."

Often at the village traffic light, a middle-aged guy smiles and waves at people while leaning against a giant cross made of deck planks. It's pointless and extremely annoying. I'm just trying to get from point A to B, I don't need to see that kind of nonsense. A lot of people driving past wave back, which I find infuriating as it just encourages him. I always give him the finger - to which he responds by smiling bigger and waving more enthusiastically as if he's in a play. It really pisses me off. I honestly hope someone loses control of their vehicle one day and takes him and his planks out.

There were no fireworks last night. A few people raged against the machine by setting off illegal crackers in their backyards, but it was a restrained New Year's. It's almost like 2020 slowly blended with 2021 rather than having defined stopping and starting points. Last year, I was with my partner Holly and offspring Seb in Seattle. We watched fireworks go off over the Space Needle and waved pink illuminated T-Mobile noodles among a crowd of thousands. The year before, my Australian friend Ross visited the United States and we watched the ball drop in Times Square.

The worst New Year's event I've attended was in 1995, in Adelaide, South Australia. The Adelaide City Council sets off fireworks from the end of a long jetty and, as it's summer in Australia this time of the year, large crowds pack the beaches. It's impossible to get a good spot, unless you get there hours early, so many families just spend the day camped out.

The best view is had by those sitting on surfboards near the end of the jetty. There's no way I'd dangle my legs over the side of a surfboard in the dark though. Certainly not in South Australian waters; the sharks there are the size of buses. People use kayaks as well as surfboards to watch the fireworks from, but, again, how much protection does a kayak give you? One nudge and you're in. I don't know why the idea of sharks in the dark is so much worse than in daytime, it just is. I won't even swim in pools at night.

I was at university at the time and a guy named Peter invited a small group of us to watch the fireworks from his father's boat. If someone invites a group out on a boat, especially 'their father's boat', it's fair to assume the boat is the type with a big motor on the back and seats and maybe a small downstairs area with a toilet - not an aluminium dinghy. Peter had stated there was room for six, but I thought that was some kind of maximum occupancy thing for safety reasons, not that there was literally only room for six people. There were no life vests and the dinghy sat very low in the water. There was a motor, but it was a little electric one that you had to clamp onto the back and it barely made a mile per hour.

We launched at twilight, from a ramp a mile or so from the jetty, and were only halfway there when the fireworks began. The last thing you want to hear when you're in an overcrowded dinghy, in the dark, half a mile from your destination and hundreds of feet from shore, is, "Big wave!"

The wave hit the side of the dinghy and splashed over us. Someone panicked and tried to stand, causing the dinghy to rock. The starboard side dipped below the water line and water poured in. It took only seconds for the dinghy to fill.

Years earlier, I'd read that passengers on the Titanic who didn't get far enough away from the ship as it went under, were sucked down with it. I'm not sure why I thought this applied to all vessels, but I wasn't going to be sucked down. I jumped and swam. Another wave crashed over me and I was underwater. I opened my eyes, looking for the surface, but everything was black. I panicked. I think I yelled. I swam, not knowing if I was swimming up, deeper, or further out, expecting teeth to close around me at any moment. I changed direction, swam harder, changed direction again.

I've also read that there's a bay in Japan that's renowned for its considerable number of suicides each year. People swim out at night, take a deep breath, then swim straight down as hard as they can. By the time their survival instincts kick in, it's too late; they can't find the surface and drown. Apparently drowning is meant to be a 'peaceful' way to go, but to be so lost, so done and empty, that you'd swim downwards into darkness, is the saddest and most horrific way to go that I can think of.

Maybe there is something to the 'peaceful' part though. There was a moment when I knew I wasn't going to find the surface, when I stopped panicking, stopped swimming.

A moment where I knew this was how I died. I've heard that your whole life flashes before your eyes when you die; it's your synapses sparking out or something - like when television sets from the seventies were switched off and the image shrunk into a thin bright light before disappearing. Others have stated their last thoughts were of those most important to them - that they saw their faces close up, their pores, the smell of their hair. I think that's nicer than a highlights reel.

My last thoughts were of the Apple Macintosh IIfx that I'd purchsed just a few days before - that it wouldn't be mine anymore, that someone else would get it. I'm not sure if that's a statement of how little there was in my life, or how much I really liked that computer. Probably both.

Thirty-odd years later, I hope I don't see a computer when I die. I hope I see Holly and Seb's faces and my synapses spark out with some kind of 'thumbs up' message that they will be fine. I don't care who uses my computer after I'm dead as long as my browser history is wiped first.

I saw a flash of blue light *below* me. More flashes, red and purple, followed by a brighter orange. I swam towards the lights and broke the surface, gasping for air and sobbing. Another firework lit up the area, white and green. Treading water, I turned and saw the others, some swimming, some walking waist deep, towards the shore. Something touched my leg.

There's nothing on the planet that makes you swim faster than something touching your leg. It's probably an ancestral memory thing from when we were fish. I bodysurfed a wave the last thirty feet or so to shore.

A few days later, Peter asked us each to pay $280 to replace his father's dinghy. I thought it was an outrageous request but, for some inexplicable reason, everyone else paid without question. I was a bit annoyed about this as it gave Peter the "everyone else has paid" argument. Not that I would have paid even if he had several arguments, but it created factions; there were the ones who understood the loss occurred during a group activity, and there was David who claimed something touched his leg.

At one point Peter sent me an official invoice. I knew it was an official invoice, because he wrote Official Invoice at the top in 42pt Helvetica Neue Bold. I sent him one back - with Super Official Invoice written in 72pt Helvetica Neue *Extra* Bold - for pain and suffering due to negligence and total disregard for passenger safety. I was seeking $10,000, but he never paid.

I'm fairly sure it was Peter who keyed my car and smeared dog poo on the door handle. Either him or Sonia Guglielmi who I was kind of seeing but broke up with because she had bad breath. Maybe I should have just used the 'it's not you, it's me' line, but if my breath is ever one-fiftieth as bad, I'd want someone to tell me.

"You're breaking up with me because I have bad breath? "

"Yes, it's dreadful."

"Why are you really breaking up with me?"

"I don't think you understand. It's not the normal 'brush your teeth and it's fixed' kind of bad breath. It's like it comes from further down, way past your mouth, past your stomach even, maybe your bowels. It's almost solid. I have to wash my clothes after we hang out. Mainly shirts, I can go two or three dates without washing my pants."

'Wow."

"You asked."

"You could have just offered me a mint."

"A mint won't cut it."

The second worst New Year's Eve I've had was when I was seven and my family were invited to another family's house for a party. While my parents were outside mingling and eating fondue, two older boys rolled me up in a floor rug, wedged it between a wardrobe and a wall, and left me there for well over an hour. I cried the entire time and wet myself. To this day I can't stand being in confined spaces. I can't even handle being in a sleeping bag. I take a doona when I go camping.

When I was eventually rescued - by a wayward partygoer searching for a bathroom - I asked my parents why they hadn't looked for me and was told they thought another kid at the party was me because we were both wearing yellow t-shirts.

This New Year's Eve, Holly invited her parents over for dinner and drinks. As such, it was less of a celebration than an exclamation mark of how removed we are from friends, travel, and excuses not to hang out with Holly's parents. They're just dreadful. Tom has no hobbies or interests - apart from watching television and wearing really tall trucker caps* - and Maria works for a company that manufactures packaging tape, but spends most of her working hours sharing political memes and conspiracy theories on Facebook.

"So, what have you been up to, Tom?"
"Nothing."
"Living the dream. What about you, Maria? Anything exciting happening in the field of polymer-based adhesives?"
"I think someone at work is trying to poison me."
"That's understandable."

We ate outside, on a snow-covered deck in face-freezing wind, as Tom and Maria aren't allowed in our house. They're the old people you see in supermarkets without a mask, breathing all over the broccoli, smug in the knowledge that everyone else is brainwashed because Tucker Carlson's hair visited them in a dream and showed them the truth.

---

* Honestly, just push it down a bit, Tom. Your scalp and the top of the cap doesn't require twelve inches of clearance. It can't be convenient - you're continually knocking the cap off when you walk through doorways - and you look like you're shoplifting a cantaloupe.

"And that's the real reason nobody is allowed to visit their loved ones in hospital. They're not really sick, they're being harvested for organs by rich Liberals. Bill Clinton has changed all of his organs several times over. He's 800 years old."

I read about a study at Harvard in the 1950s, where researchers placed rats in a pool of water to test how long they could tread water. It seems kind of pointless and cruel but the scientists might have been bored or something. On average, the rats gave up and sank after 15 minutes. But, right before they drowned, the researchers plucked them out, dried them off, and let them rest for a few minutes. Then they put them back in for a second round. This time, the rats treaded water for *sixty* hours. The conclusion drawn was that since the rats *believed* they would eventually be rescued, they were able to push their bodies way past what they previously thought impossible.

There were *some* festivities at our house last night; I cheered when Tom and Maria left.

I also sent a group message stating 'Happy New Year' to my contacts list. It included an emoji of a cork popping out of a bottle. Ross responded with eighteen lines of cocktail emojis and eggplants, my coworker Walter wrote 'Hnt2u2', and Brian - a guy I sold a used treadmill to on Craigslist two years ago - sent me a photo of his penis.

Thankfully, the new Covid vaccines will be available any month now, and we can all get back to normal. I'm guessing it will be all be over by March. My coworker Ben suggested it could take longer, as some people might refuse to get the vaccine, but why would anyone want this dragging on any longer than it has to? There's no reason for groundless pessimism; people are inherently good, trust science, and will always choose the wellbeing of others over selfish or political motivations.

Update:

I've given my New Year's resolution some thought. As it's good to have a goal but at the same time not create an unrealistic task for yourself, I've chosen 'try to be kinder to squirrels.'

JAN 2021

2

SATURDAY

Brian apologised for sending me a photo of his penis. He's embarrassed about the whole thing and explained he'd had a lot to drink, wasn't wearing his reading glasses, and thought the message was from someone named Dani. He also asked me to delete the photo which was kind of odd. What makes him think I'd keep it?

"How's the deck you're building coming along, David? Do you have any photos?"
"Sure... here's one of the posts going in... and this is the framework being added... that belongs to the guy who bought our treadmill... and here you can see the first planks going down. We went with a composite for its durability and UV rating."

I don't think I've ever sent anybody a photo of my penis. It seems like something I'd remember doing. I certainly wouldn't send one without someone specifically requesting it. Even then, if I were inclined to facilitate the request, I'd just send a picture of someone else's from the Internet. I'd pick a similar shade but nicer shape. Perhaps something tapered.

I have sent the wrong person a message before, but there were no penises involved. When Seb was nine, I collected him and two of his friends from after-school lacrosse practice. The boys were siblings and their mother, Terri, knew I'd be dropping them home afterwards. Regardless, I sent her a message to let her know the boys were with me but accidently sent a guy named Terry - a work client - the message, "I have your kids."

I also once sent my dentist a photo of myself - trying on a shirt in a changing room - with the message, "It fits well but I'm not sure about the colour." The message was intended for Holly but my dentist replied, "I like the color. Go for it." I had to find a different dentist after that. Not because of the shirt thing, it turned out he'd been fondling women patients while they were under anesthetic and his clinic was shut down. I was pretty happy about it because I owed them money and wasn't a fan of their waiting room setup.

Several years back, our office manager at the time, Sharon, mistakenly selected 'Staff' instead of 'Steve', and sent a photo of herself wearing only pigtails to the entire office. As she was a huge heifer, the thing that impressed me most about the selfie was her flexibility. There's no way I could get my feet behind my head like that, even with a pillow under my back. I've tried. While I understand Sharon's decision to leave without notice, the subject matter was actually less embarrassing than the environment the photo was taken in. Her bedroom had green striped wallpaper and a ruffled floral bedspread. A stained-glass lamp shaped like a butterfly was just visible amongst a throng of teddy bears on a side table, and above the bed was a poster of a tiger. If that were my bedroom, I wouldn't be taking nude selfies, I'd be weeping as I splashed kerosene about and lit a match.

Also, I just re-read yesterday's bit regarding Tom, and I don't think I was particularly successful in getting across just how high he wears his trucker caps. You likely thought it was an exaggeration as there's only so much height that can possibly be achieved. As such I've decided to include a scale drawing. I don't generally include illustrations in my books, as I'm not overly artistic, but I believe this captures Tom's signature look perfectly:

JAN   2021

3
SUNDAY

Holly printed a return label this morning - for an Apple Watch she bought me for Christmas. I did try using it, I thought it might motivate me to lose a few pounds, but I forgot how much I hate being told what to do.

"Time to stand up."
"Time to see how impact resistant you are."

Our printer is one of those 'all in one' machines and I forgot to remove my drawing of Tom after scanning it. The fact that Holly knew it was a drawing of her father means it's a pretty accurate representation, so, with a newfound confidence in my artistic abilities, here's another drawing titled *Don't lie, it's not a skateboard with a wind flap. Why would a skateboard have a face and ears?*

JAN 2021
4
MONDAY

It snowed last night. A lot. There's no 'things' outside, everything is just a series of white curvy bumps. It's also quiet; with no cars on the streets or people doing people things, it's as if someone hit a pause button. I think it was the quiet that woke me - it's only 5am - it won't be this way for long though. Soon, the sound of snowplows will break the silence as their metal blades scrape across asphalt, clearing the roads for people to get to work.

There was mention of everyone at the agency going in to the office today - to "regroup and start the year as a unified team." That's not going to happen. Similar statements have been made dozens of times over the last several months but then someone's dog needs to go to the vet, or they ate questionable sushi, or their washing machine hose broke and flooded the apartment. Gary, our account manager, has the best excuses; while most of the staff simply state they aren't feeling well or have a dentist appointment, Gary feels it necessary to provide explicit details such as, "I know we planned to come into the office today, but I have severe diarrhea. There's also a bit of blood."

Last year, Gary sent an email explaining that he couldn't attend that day's planned regroup meeting because he shot a burglar.

Apparently, he got up in the middle of the night to use the bathroom, glanced out the window, and saw a light moving about in his garden shed. By looking at Gary, you wouldn't peg him as someone with a home arsenal that would give Rambo an erection, but that's a thing with Americans; you can't tell which ones can kill you at any moment. Some Americans walk around with guns in holsters, as if they never grew out of the wanting to be a cowboy phase, but they're not necessarily the ones you have to worry about. It's the grandma in Walmart or the guy collecting trolleys at Food Lion. They're packing heat because "it's better to need a gun and have it than to not have it when you need it" or something. In their minds, being armed creates a level playing field, a playing field where the ultimate game outcome is saving the day and being the hero. Unfortunately, this means that if you're ever in an 'active shooter' situation, any direction you run away in will have an Edith and Brandon returning fire.

Gary probably did a little fist pump and whispered, "Yes!" when he saw movement in the shed. I like to imagine he pressed a secret button and a wall slid open to reveal shelves of automatic weapons, maybe some grenades and a bazooka, but apparently he just keeps a few handguns hidden around the house and one in his nightstand.

"You have guns hidden around your house?"

"Yes, of course. I'm not going to be the victim if someone breaks into my home to rob me."

"Where are they hidden? Is one taped under your desk like in the movies?"

"I'm not telling you where they are."

"Oh my god, you have one taped under your desk, don't you?"

"No, they're hidden far more strategically. My desk is upstairs."

"You could offer to write the robber a cheque."

"Or, and this is just one example, I could act like I'm having chest pain and need my heart pills."

"You're going to put on a play for the burglar?"

"Not a play, a ruse."

"And you have a gun hidden in your medicine cabinet?"

"No, the pills are in a kitchen cupboard. Next to a box of Pop-Tarts."

I've been to Gary's house. I once had to drive him home and help him inside after he developed edema and his feet ballooned to four times their normal size - they looked like footballs with toes. Gary's house is a two-bedroom, one-bathroom home, in a town called Friendly. There's a dead tree and a big rock painted yellow in the front yard. Nobody is casing the joint to steal Gary's jewels. He doesn't own a Rolex collection or have Rembrandts hanging in his hallway. He does have a glass display cabinet in his living room for collectibles, but I doubt there's a huge black market for 1:24 scale diecast Nascar vehicles.

"Tell me where the jewels are!"

"I don't have any jewels."

"Fine. I'm taking this Dale Earnhardt #8 *United For America* diecast model then."

"Ahhh, I'm having chest pain. Untie my ropes so I can get to my heart pills."

"I'm not untying you. I'll get your pills for you though. Where are they?"

"Never mind. The chest pain stopped. I do need to write a cheque though."

In Gary's first retelling of the burglar shooting, he was basically John Wick; he surprised the burglar, who ran, and Gary shot him as he jumped the back fence. With further prompting for details, however, the action hero veneer peeled pretty quickly.

"You shot someone over a bag of lawn seed?"

"It was dark, I couldn't tell what he was carrying. Besides, stealing is stealing. Today it's a bag of lawn seed, tomorrow, who knows."

"Maybe a leaf blower or a rake. Was he badly hurt?"

"How would I know? He ran off."

"He ran off? What makes you think you hit him then? Was there any blood?"

"No, but I looked over the fence and saw him running up the street with a limp."

"A limp?"

"Yes, I would have chased after him but the fence is tall and

I didn't have shoes on."

"Honestly, worst story ever. You probably missed and he hurt his leg jumping the fence."

"That's what the police said."

"I was actually concerned for you. I thought you might have PTSD or something after shooting another human being, but it was just a waste of empathy. I'm surprised you even bothered calling the police."

"I didn't, my neighbors did. Discharging a firearm in city limits is a class 4 misdemeanor. I have to go to court next month."

I was right about the regroup not happening today. Ben emailed that he has a thousand things to do, Jodie, our senior designer, has a migraine, and Gary has an in-grown hair on his chest that he thinks may be infected because it's sore to touch and is seeping. He's going to try to cut it out with a scalpel. The regroup has been changed to this Friday instead.

We all have stuff to go on with in the meantime; Ben has copy for a range of shower heads by Moen to write, Jodie is working on the packaging. Walter has a twelve-page brochure about window blinds to design, and Mike, our creative director, is writing a job description for the currently vacant HR position. We lost Jennifer to Covid last year and she and Mike were close. It took him six months to even consider refilling the role and he's been writing the job description since last October.

It shouldn't take four months to write a job description, regardless of how much you don't want to write it. I don't particularly want to do anything but there's only so long I can stretch doing nothing out for. There's a fine line between, "David hasn't finished that yet?" and "Does David still work here?" I understand Mike is sad about replacing Jennifer, but we all have to do things that make us sad. Holly asks me to do things that make me sad all the time. Like taking the dogs for a walk or giving her a foot rub. Do I complain about it? Sure, but do I do it anyway? No, but I pay my taxes.

The roads have been cleared of snow and it's loud outside. There's the sound of traffic and kids playing and the *sssht sssht sssht* of neighbors shoveling snow from their sidewalks. It's village law that we have to clear snow from the sidewalk in front of our house within an hour of the snow stopping. If we don't, the village elders whip us with a willow branch.

I make my offspring Seb shovel ours because the one time I did, a neighbour waved at me. We're not friends, Ian, you let your dog bark constantly and your backyard looks like the internment camp in *District 9*. Do a dump-run and buy a shock-collar. I don't care if it's cruel, after hearing your dog bark for eight hours straight, I'd happily zap it in the face with a cattle prod.

I'm meant to be working on a logo today, but I can't concentrate with all the *sssht sssht ssshting,* so Seb and I are going to watch a documentary about bats instead.

JAN   2021

5
TUESDAY

The documentary about bats wasn't that good. I thought I might learn something new about bats but I guess if you've seen one documentary about bats, you've seen them all. There's only so much ground you can cover really; we all know bats can see moths with their ears. Seb and I also watched a documentary about flamingos and one about crabs. I did learn a few things about crabs, but I don't foresee any possible future conversation where that knowledge will be useful.

"Crabs are decapods, meaning they have ten legs, and can reach speeds of up to 20mph."
"What's that got to do with catching a cab?"
"I thought you said catch a crab."

Seb brought home about fifty documentaries on 4k Blu-ray from Best Buy recently. He gets a staff discount.

One of the many benefits of the pandemic was that Seb flew from Australia to the United States early last year, and wasn't allowed to fly back. It meant he overstayed his tourist Visa, so was technically an illegal alien, but ICE doesn't give a fuck unless you look Mexican. Nobody is separating Swedish families and locking their blonde haired, blue eyed kids up in cages.

"Snälla, jag vill bara ha min mamma och pappa."
"Shut it, Birkenstock, be thankful for your Utåker bed and Tjärblomster blanket."
"Min filt kliar och jag är olycklig."

And yes, I realize Birkenstock is a German brand, not Swedish. I originally wrote Hasselblad, which *is* a Swedish brand, but Seb read the first draft and asked if Hasselblad is Swedish for someone with a bladder problem, so I changed it. I could have used IKEA of course, but then I would have had to change the bed and blanket name bit and I don't know enough about Sweden to come up with another joke. I do know Volvos, ABBA, and Greta Thunberg come from Sweden, and that all Swedish women, apart from Greta Thunberg, play volleyball, but that's about the extent of my knowledge.

I'm making an assumption of course; Greta may play volleyball when she's not waving at penguins or whatever it is she does. And, just so I don't receive dozens of emails telling me off for belittling the important work Greta is doing, I'm fully aware that climate change is a very real threat and that it is our collective and individual responsibility to preserve the planet on which we all live. I just think she'd be a lot prettier if she smiled more.

I actually dated an environmental activist once. At least I thought we were dating. Her name was Yolanda, which is Polish for 'unwashed'. We spent 14 hours chained to a tree on a housing development before she informed me she was a lesbian and had just needed a ride. It's not easy getting a refund for Greenpeace membership. I had to ring my bank and dispute the credit card charge. I did get to keep the T-shirt though. Really, I deserved it for everything I'd done for the environment. There was a lot of sap on that tree.

Seb decided to stay in the United States, applied for residency, and received his green card a few months back. This meant he could get a job and stop being a parasite. That may seem harsh, but how many packets of Oreos and cans of Coke can one person possibly consume in a day? You're probably thinking, "Well, if they were starving or it was a competition, maybe twenty packets and a hundred cans?" Which is way more than he does consume and I doubt anyone could manage that.

Four mornings per week, Seb dons his blue shirt, straightens his yellow name tag, and I drive him to the mall. He's meant to be saving for a car, but the Best Buy employee discount is like crack.

"A USB mini-fridge? Really?"
"Yes, for my room. So I don't have to keep going downstairs to get Cokes. With employee discount, it was only $149.95. It also has a Bluetooth speaker."

A few weeks back, Seb changed all the light switches in our house. We can't just flick the lights on or off anymore, we have to download an app. He also changed the light bulbs for smarter light bulbs, and swapped our door lock for one that whirrs and beeps and sends text messages if you forget your eighteen-character code that has to include a capital letter and special character. A talking box controls everything now. We're basically living inside a robot that doesn't understand Australian accents.

"Alexa, turn on the television."
"Purging oxygen."
"Cancel that please."
"Setting oven to 450 degrees."
For the past twelve months, Seb has described the television in our living room as 'Victorian'.

"It's like watching a gif. The pixels are the size of stamps."
"Not if you squint."
"It also has the thickest bezel I've ever seen, it's like a picture frame. What is that, like four inches?"
"You can't see the bezel when the lights are off."
"It's still there."

When I was young, our family had a 21" Rank Arena television set. My sister and I were the remote. I think we had that television for ten years and nobody ever complained about the dots per inch. You got what you got. If you sat close, you could see the images were made of red, green, and blue blurry lines, but we weren't supposed to sit close, because televisions back then caused face cancer. I think everything caused face cancer back then. That's the problem with kids nowadays; not enough face cancer. There's no reason for them not to spend hours staring at big screens, little screens, and computer screens. I didn't have any screens of my own when I was a kid, I had to create my own entertainment. I made outfits for sticks and pretended they were the little humans from the show *Land of the Giants*.

Seb's complaints about our television became incessant once he started working at Best Buy. He became Professor Television and endlessly quoted model specs that only people who vape or wakeboard care about.

"And that's just eighteen reasons why we should buy the Sony 9680 4K Spazmatron. Additionally, it has 1200 quadbikes of nanotoasters and a refresh rate of 9000 gigaberries. That's important for watching shows about ducks with all the lights on."
"Seb, it's 3am. I was having a nice dream about horses."

I saw a movie a few years back called *The Chronicles of Riddick* and there's a scene in it where a guy walks outside and melts. I think it was on another planet, one closer to the sun. I can't remember the reason the guy walked outside, perhaps he was sad, but he stood, bracing against the heat, for as long as possible before collapsing. Seb's television spec onslaught was kind of like that. We bought a new television and the picture quality is better than our old television, but I've been pretending I can't see a difference.

"What are you talking about? It's 4K! It's four times better than the old television."

"Well, as long as you're happy with the amount of Ks."

"No, admit the picture quality is a lot better."

"I honestly can't tell any difference. The bezel is definitely thinner though."

"Right, I'm going to bring a couple of 4K documentaries home from work so you get a proper representation. They're the ones we display in store to showcase the picture quality."

"I'm not a huge fan of documentaries."

"You'll like these ones. There's one about bats. Did you know they can see moths with their ears?"

"Yes."

Also, I should also mention that the television swap wasn't as simple as unplugging the old one and plugging in the new one. Seb's staff discount saved us about $300, but the new television refused to communicate with our existing sound system so we had to upgrade that as well. And the cables. And the cable box.

We ended up spending double what the television cost. We also have to use three remotes now; one for changing channels, one for the volume, and another to turn everything on and off. It's worth it to see bats catching moths in more Ks though.

JAN 2021
6
WEDNESDAY

I vaguely remember, four years ago, when those questioning the results of the election were labelled 'snowflakes'.

I have the news on in the background. A snowflake parade is currently being held in honor of the world's biggest snowflake. Honestly, if everyone were wearing snowflake costumes and holding big snowflakes on sticks, it couldn't be more snowflakey.

My friend JM is at the snowflake parade. I looked for him in the crowd but couldn't see him. He probably got his free lectern, killed a policeman, and left.

From: Mike Campbell
Date: Thursday 7 January 2021 2.19pm
To: David Thorne
Subject: workload

David,

With the current workload, I agree we need an additional graphic designer. Use the existing job description to post the position but reduce the salary to 35K.

Mike

....

From: David Thorne
Date: Thursday 7 January 2021 2.24pm
To: Mike Campbell
Subject: Re: workload

Mike,

Why pay them at all? Graphic designers don't need to eat, they survive on compliments and Pantone swatches.

David

From: Mike Campbell
Date: Thursday 7 January 2021 2.30pm
To: David Thorne
Subject: Re: Re: workload

What is Walter currently on? 40K?

Mike

....

From: David Thorne
Date: Thursday 7 January 2021 2.43pm
To: Mike Campbell
Subject: Re: Re: Re: workload

Mike,

Walter is currently on 47K. You approved his pay increase last year after attending an event at his house and stating, "Nobody should have to live in this squalor." You also swore you'd seen the house on the news.

It was Walter's birthday party. You gave him a tie.

Entry-level salary for a junior designer is around 40K. Advertising the position for less than that will be reflected by the quality of applicants.

43K would be more appropriate.

David

From: Mike Campbell
Date: Thursday 7 January 2021 2.55pm
To: David Thorne
Subject: Re: Re: Re: Re: workload

Was I wrong about his house? Who lives like that? There was a barrel in his living room.

Graphic designers are disposable at the moment. The guy who made my sandwich at Subway last week used to work for Foster Web Marketing as a senior designer. He's still on their website. He asked if we were hiring. I said no because he has a wispy beard.

Make it 35K.

Mike

....

From: David Thorne
Date: Thursday 7 January 2021 3.02pm
To: Mike Campbell
Subject: Re: Re: Re: Re: Re: workload

Mike,

It's a wine barrel conversation table. Not everyone shops exclusively at Herman Miller. I'm going to post the salary as 43K.

David

From: Mike Campbell
Date: Thursday 7 January 2021 3.11pm
To: David Thorne
Subject: Re: Re: Re: Re: Re: Re: workload

No, you're not. Make it 35K. I guarantee we'll have plenty of applicants.

And fuck off it was a wine barrel conversation table. That makes it sound like he got it at Pottery Barn. It was just a barrel we stood around because there weren't any chairs. It was like being in a squatter's house.

Mike

....

From: David Thorne
Date: Thursday 7 January 2021 3.18pm
To: Mike Campbell
Subject: Re: Re: Re: Re: Re: Re: Re: workload

Mike,

It's not the number of applicants I'm concerned about, it's having to wade through portfolios consisting entirely of newsletters put together in Word during the applicant's last job as a school secretary fifteen years ago.

Are you going to be involved in the selection process?

David

From: Mike Campbell
Date: Thursday 7 January 2021 3.25pm
To: David Thorne
Subject: Re: Re: Re: Re: Re: Re: Re: Re: workload

I don't need to be involved. You and Jodie are capable. It's a graphic design position, not strategic branding. Any halfwit can move text around in InDesign. Just pick someone that doesn't take a week to draw a circle. We don't need another Aaron situation.*

Post the salary as 35K. End of discussion.

Mike

....

From: David Thorne
Date: Thursday 7 January 2021 3.29pm
To: Mike Campbell
Subject: Re: Re: Re: Re: Re: Re: Re: Re: Re: workload

Sigh. Okay.

---

* *Aaron was only at the agency for two weeks as he wasn't quite the experienced designer he made himself out to be in his resume. When called out for taking two days to turn a colour image to greyscale, he resigned, declared everyone at the agency to be a "pretentious wanker", and kicked the photocopier on his way out. It left a decent dent. Later that night, early morning really, Aaron returned with a brick. He attempted to throw it through the foyer window but it bounced off. I have the security footage saved to my phone and watch it occasionally for a chuckle.*

From: Mike Campbell
Date: Thursday 7 January 2021 3.37pm
To: David Thorne
Subject: Sigh?

Why would you write 'sigh' in an email?

Shrug. That's me shrugging to express how much I care about your sigh.

Mike

....

From: David Thorne
Date: Thursday 7 January 2021 3.42pm
To: Mike Campbell
Subject: Re: Sigh?

Raises an eyebrow. Speaking of filling positions, how are you doing with the HR job description?

David

....

From: Mike Campbell
Date: Thursday 7 January 2021 3.46pm
To: David Thorne
Subject: Re: Re: Sigh?

Fires David. I have a lot on my plate at the moment.

Mike

From: David Thorne
Date: Thursday 7 January 2021 3.49pm
To: Mike Campbell
Subject: Re: Re: Re: Sigh?

I'm happy to look at it next week if you'd prefer.

David

....

From: Mike Campbell
Date: Thursday 7 January 2021 3.55pm
To: David Thorne
Subject: Re: Re: Re: Re: Sigh?

No, I'm going to write it. Writing it is the easy part.

Are we still having the regroup meeting tomorrow? If not, I
might book a massage. Patrick made me do a 5k fun run and
I'm crippled.

Mike

....

From: David Thorne
Date: Thursday 7 January 2021 4.03pm
To: Mike Campbell
Subject: Re: Re: Re: Re: Re: Sigh?

I'm fine with rescheduling.

David

JAN **2021**

8

FRIDAY

From: Gary Wright
Date: Friday 8 January 2021 8.16am
To: All Staff
Subject: Regroup

Good morning,

I know we were planning to regroup today but I have a doctor's appointment at 10.30.

I tried cutting the ingrown hair out of my chest and it's definitely infected now. It's green and purple and almost an inch across and won't stop seeping. I had to sleep on my back last night and I'm usually a side sleeper.

I'm going to use two pieces of foam to keep the seatbelt away from the area when Julie drives me to the doctor. I'd drive myself but I took an oxycodone when I got up. I'm sure I'd be fine but the packet says not to drive and it's better to be safe than sorry.

Gary

JAN 2021

9

SATURDAY

Best Buy has some kind of special deal on mobile telephones this weekend, so Seb is looking at upgrading mine.

This means I'll probably need three telephones; one to answer calls, one to call out, and one for messaging. It might also entail upgrading all the plugs in the walls, replacing the electrical wiring throughout, and launching my own telecommunications satellite.

Update

I have a new telephone. It's identical to my old telephone but has a slightly thinner bezel. It's like looking into the future.

"How long have I been frozen?"
"5000 years. Welcome to the year 7021."
"Oh my god. I bet so much has changed."
"Yes, you may want to sit down for this... telephone bezels are 14% thinner. Also bears evolved. They live on the moon now. It's theirs. There was a war."

JAN 2021
10
SUNDAY

Since I was about ten, I've had a recurring dream about 'pool spiders'. Basically, I'm in an Olympic sized pool, swimming underwater looking up, and the entire surface - apart from a hole about four feet wide - is covered in black spiders. They're about hand-sized and can walk on water. I stay underwater for as long as can, then surface at the hole to take a breath. The spiders rush towards me, some reaching my head, and I go back under, frantically clearing the spiders from my hair and face, then look for the hole again.

I've had the dream for so many years, I don't know when I became inured to it. At some point 'Dear god, pool spiders!' became 'Really? Pool spiders again?' and now I just go through the motions. I know that swimming down and kicking off the bottom creates a larger splash when I surface, making it harder for the spiders to run towards me. I can also swim faster naked, so I usually ditch my boardshorts.

You become desensitized to anything that's repeated often enough. Even the worst of things. Abused children learn to disconnect, American parents send their children to schools, and Seb and I sit and nod every time Holly's father, Tom, tells us his rusty hinge story.

"David, did I tell you I fixed our back door?"

"Yes."

"The hinges were rusty so I drove to Home Depot and bought a tub of Navel Jelly rust dissolver for $6.75 - that's cheaper than buying a three pack of new hinges for $10."

"Yes, $3.15 cheaper. You could buy a hotdog."

"Excellent stuff that Navel Jelly, took the rust right off. The hinges are like new. Do you have any rusty hinges?"

"Not at the moment."

"Well, if any get rusty, don't buy new hinges because I still have three-quarters of a tub of Navel Jelly left. It goes a long way."

"I'll keep that in mind. Thanks."

"No problem. You only need a little bit. No need to slather it on. Takes about ten minutes and the hinges come out looking new. It's not just for hinges though, it also works on bolts."

"Really? Bolts don't require a different type of rust remover? One specially for bolts?"

"No, it will work on bolts. Do you have any rusty bolts?"

"Not that I'm aware of."

"Well, if any get rusty, don't buy new bolts because I still have three-quarters of a tub of Navel Jelly left. It goes a long way. Seb, did I tell you I fixed our back door?"

"Yes."

"The hinges were rusty."

Tom and Maria visited Gatlinburg in 2015 and apparently saw a really big pumpkin. If you ever visit Gatlinburg, you needn't bother with the standard tourist attractions like Dollywood or the Aerial Tramway, because it's the big pumpkins that create real memories. I've heard the really big pumpkin story at least fifty times and, with each retelling, the pumpkin gets slightly larger.

"Did I tell you about the time Maria and I visited Gatlinburg and saw a pumpkin as big as beachball? I couldn't reach my arms all the way around it. I wish I'd taken a photo."

"Have you seen those red balls outside of Target stores? The pumpkin was twice the size of one of those."

"Easily as big as a three-person tent."

"I climbed it. There was a ladder."

"If you carved it out, a family of four could live inside quite comfortably."

"It took three months and four days to circumnavigate. Half our expedition died."

"The sun? Pfft."

Holly and I have been to Gatlinburg. I wasn't that impressed. Maybe because we didn't see any really big pumpkins. We did ride the Aerial Tram up and back down though. We also visited the aquarium. They had four fish.

I read somewhere that there's very little difference between ten lashings* and fifty. Apparently the first lashing isn't the worst, it's the second, then, by the sixth or seventh, your brain says, "Okay, I'm out, let me know how the rest of your day goes."

I was forced to go to Sunday school when I was about nine. My parents weren't religious, they just wanted me out of the house. Once, while colouring an illustration of two devils poking damned souls with pitchforks, I asked Father George, "Wouldn't you just get used to the flames after a while?"

"Sorry, David?"
"The flames. If you're burning forever, after a while you'd get used to it."
"No, because just when you're getting used to the flames, Satan turns them off and lets you cool down. Then he turns them back on again."

Logically, it makes sense I suppose. When I'm in the shower and Seb or Holly use the washing machine or dishwasher, it's pretty much what I imagine Hell would be like. Also, on that topic, as the washing machine and the dishwasher in our house share the same water supply, if you put them both on

---

* *The being whipped kind of lashing, not the securing two or more items together with rope type. There'd be a noticeable difference between ten items lashed together with rope and fifty. It would require more space.*

at the same time, they each run at 50% capacity. This results in the dishes and clothes being 50% clean. It's not rocket science. How hard is it understand this?

"Seb, are you using the washing machine?"
"Yes, I have to work tomorrow and my Best Buy shirt is dirty."
"The dishwasher is on."
"So?"
"We've had this conversation a hundred times. The dishes don't get clean if the washing machine is on at the same time. Look, this plate still has cheese on it. Cheese is the easiest thing for dishwashers to remove because it melts."
"That's not how it works, they both still wash the same, they just take twice as long."
"That's clearly not true. We have the cheese as evidence. Enjoy wearing a half-washed shirt tomorrow. Good luck getting any apps."

Father George also informed me that the toads which rained down during one of the plagues were mean and had sharp teeth, so no, you couldn't keep them as pets, and that Jesus created Atari. He also once asked me, while I was helping him stack *Good News* Bibles in the stationery room, if my penis sometimes gets bigger when I wash it in the shower.

A short time later, my parents told me I didn't have to attend Sunday school any more. I was happy about that for a few weekends but then they signed me up for Scouts.

Years later, I learned that Father George had asked other kids the shower question. I don't think he stuck his finger up kid's butts or anything, but he was moved to a different church in a different town and our town got a new chaplain. He's the one that stuck his finger up kid's butts.

The church must have them on rotation or something because our town went through three or four chaplains over the space of just a few years.

"Okay, Father Darryl, we're moving you to Peterborough and Father Craig is moving to Leigh Creek."
"Peterborough? Why?"
"You fingered twelve kids, Darryl. Look, I get it, young boys are seriously hot, but try to be a bit more subtle about it next time."
"Okay, but I've spent three months grooming a blonde boy named Alex. Can I at least have another week?"
"No, but I'm sure Father Craig will appreciate your efforts. Best not to think of these moves as punishment, but rather as opportunities. Soft, warm, sexy opportunities. With buttholes. I'm keeping these Polaroids by the way."

My best friend at the time, Matthew, was one of the kids that was molested by Father Darryl. He wasn't actually fingered, Father Daryl just sucked him off. I wasn't meant to know about it but my mother and Matthew's mother were friends and I heard them discussing it over coffee. The police were involved and a social worker made Matthew point to the crotch of a Cabbage Patch doll. When I asked Matthew what it had felt like, he told me, "Kind of like when a dog licks your hand but prickly."

Also, Matthew's mom signed him up for Scouts, which meant I had someone to hang out with. I hadn't made friends with any of the kids in my troop because most were older and had lots of badges. I had one, for traffic safety, which is one more than Matthew had. He eventually earned something like three hundred merit badges and needed to wear a special sash for them all, but I was well out by then. The Scouts have something called bob-a-job where you have to weed old people's gardens. You become desensitized to *almost* anything that's repeated often enough, but not five hours of, "You have to get them by the roots otherwise they grow back."

I had the pool spider dream again last night. It's been a few months since I last had it but, finding myself underwater, reflexes kicked in and I immediately tried to ditch my boardshorts. Only I wasn't wearing boardshorts, I was wearing a suit and tie. Panicking a bit at this change in the well-established sequence, I looked up to locate the hole in the black crawling surface. There wasn't a hole.

From: David Thorne
Date: Monday 11 January 2021 9.51am
To: Melissa Peters, **Cc:** All staff
Subject: Resumés

Melissa,

The position for a new graphic designer went up this morning. Can you please forward all resumés to myself and Jodie? Thank you. We're offering the salary equivalent of a rat on a stick so I'm not expecting a huge response.

David

....

From: Walter Bowers
Date: Monday 11 January 2021 10.26am
To: David Thorne
Subject: Re: Resumés

Josh said we are looking for the graphic designer and I said I did know anything about it. Am I should have been told about so I don't hear it from other people. Its just polite.

Walter

From: David Thorne
Date: Monday 11 January 2021 10.32am
To: Walter Bowers
Subject: Re: Re: Resumés

Walter,

Do you read what you've written before hitting send? It's like the written version of a stroke. Are you referring to the post for a new graphic designer? Who's Josh?

You were in the Zoom meeting when we discussed hiring another graphic designer. You said we should hire someone who likes doing business cards because you hate doing them.

David

....

From: Walter Bowers
Date: Monday 11 January 2021 10.58am
To: David Thorne
Subject: Re: Re: Re: Resumés

I do hate doing them

....

From: David Thorne
Date: Monday 11 January 2021 11.03am
To: Walter Bowers
Subject: Re: Re: Re: Re: Resumés

Walter,

Yes, we're all aware of that. That's why we give them to you to do. What was the main gist of your email?

David

....

From: Walter Bowers
Date: Monday 11 January 2021 11.20am
To: David Thorne
Subject: Re: Re: Re: Re: Re: Resumés

All I'm saying is that you should have told me we were getting a designer. my friend Josh told me and I was I dont know nobody tells me anything. I forgot we talked about it but I didnt know we were getting someone now. I should have been told thats all. Should I be worried that Im told like are they being a replacement?

Walter

....

From: David Thorne
Date: Monday 11 January 2021 11.27am
To: Walter Bowers
Subject: Re: Re: Re: Re: Re: Re: Resumés

Walter,

We're not advertising for your replacement if that's what you're rambling about. It's a junior position to take some of the workload off you and Jodie. You'll have seniority.

You're welcome to participate in the selection process. You should really be in the interviews with Jodie and I anyway, seeing as you'll be working closely with them.

David

....

From: Walter Bowers
Date: Monday 11 January 2021 11.33am
To: David Thorne
Subject: Re: Re: Re: Re: Re: Re: Re: Resumés

Does that mean I'm going to be there boss?

Walter

....

From: David Thorne
Date: Monday 11 January 2021 11.35am
To: Walter Bowers
Subject: Re: Re: Re: Re: Re: Re: Re: Re: Resumés

Walter,

Is Jodie your boss?

David

From: Walter Bowers
Date: Monday 11 January 2021 11.42am
To: David Thorne
Subject: Re: Re: Re: Re: Re: Re: Re: Re: Re: Resumés

She acts like it. I always have to do what she says but whenever I ask her something she says shes busy. Just because your a senior designer doesnt mean you know more Shes just been her longer. I know a lot more than she does. She should say please instead of telling you. Its just polite.

....

From: David Thorne
Date: Monday 11 January 2021 11.46am
To: Walter Bowers
Subject: Re: Re: Re: Re: Re: Re: Re: Re: Re: Re: Resumés

Walter,

The new designer may view you the same way.

David

....

From: Walter Bowers
Date: Monday 11 January 2021 11.55am
To: David Thorne
Subject: Re: Re: Re: Re: Re: Re: Re: Re: Re: Re: Re: Resumés

No I'll be a kind boss.

JAN 2021
12
TUESDAY

From: Melissa Peters
Date: Tuesday 12 January 2021 10.05am
To: All Staff
Subject: Invites

Howdy Y'all :)

Andrew and I sent out the wedding invites yesterday. Make sure you keep March 6 free!

We're having a barn wedding and the theme is country rustic. The Feehan Brothers are booked so start practicing your boot scootin!

Mel

....

From: Jodie Smythe
Date: Tuesday 12 January 2021 10.11am
To: Melissa Peters
Subject: Re: Invites

Lol. Who the fuck are the Feehan Brothers?

From: Melissa Peters
Date: Tuesday 12 January 2021 10.17am
To: Jodie Smythe   **Cc:** All Staff
Subject: Re: Re: Invites

I'm ccing this so everyone can see how you speak to me.
It doesn't matter who they are because you're not invited.

Mel

....

From: Jodie Smythe
Date: Tuesday 12 January 2021 10.22am
To: Melissa Peters
Subject: Re: Re: Re: Invites

I don't care if you cc the whole world. Yeah I'm sad I don't get
to go to a farm in MARCH when it's still cold and listen to
a country band nobody's ever heard of. Enjoy your redneck
wedding in the barn with the pigs. lol

....

From: Melissa Peters
Date: Tuesday 12 January 2021 10.25am
To: Melissa Peters
Subject: Re: Re: Re: Re: Invites

There's not going to be any pigs. I already told you you're not
invited. March 6 is our anniversary. You wouldn't know
anything about anniversaries though.

From: Mike Campbell
Date: Tuesday 12 January 2021 10.32am
To: Melissa Peters, Jodie Smythe
Subject: Re: Re: Re: Re: Re: Invites

Jodie,

You started this with your comment about the music choice and we both know you're not going to come up with an insult to top Melissa's pig invite comment.

Why are you commenting about Melissa's big day anyway?

Mike

....

From: Melissa Peters
Date: Tuesday 12 January 2021 10.36am
To: Melissa Peters
Subject: Re: Re: Re: Re: Re: Re: Invites

Because she's jealous.

....

From: Jodie Smythe
Date: Tuesday 12 January 2021 10.41am
To: Melissa Peters
Subject: Re: Re: Re: Re: Re: Re: Re: Invites

Jealous of you? LOL!!!! All I did was ask who the band was.

And country rustic? Really? How creative. Who's doing the catering? Cracker Barrel?

I'm actually happy for you. I think it's great that Andrew forgave you for fucking an electrician. Not that he'd ever get anyone else with his looks. You two are made for each other.

....

From: Melissa Peters
Date: Tuesday 12 January 2021 4.06pm
To: Melissa Peters
Subject: Re: Re: Re: Re: Re: Re: Re: Re: Invites

Thank you. And don't worry I'm sure your perfect match is out there somewhere as well. Some guys like fat girls.

Mel

....

From: Walter Bowers
Date: Tuesday 12 January 2021 4.12pm
To: Melissa Peters
Subject: Re: Invites

I dont need to practice Im an excellent dancer

Do we have to buy a present?

JAN 2021
13
WEDNESDAY

Melissa and Andrew's wedding invitation came in the mail today. I find it interesting that the post office can deliver this kind of nonsense within three days but it takes six months to deliver my books anywhere. I had a guy email me last year to let me know that a copy of *The Internet is a Playground* he ordered in 2011 had just arrived. Apparently it was inscribed to his wife who died in 2016 of cancer. Better late than never though I suppose.

Melissa declined all professional offers to help design the invitation, preferring to do it herself, and it shows. There's clipart of wedding bells, cowboy boots, and a gold glitter border. She must have used a UHU stick because there's glitter everywhere now.

I've hidden the invitation from Holly. I'm not a huge fan of attending weddings as it means sitting for extended periods, socializing, and being told, "Come on, just dance with me, you never dance with me." I'm not a dancer and, despite Holly's conviction otherwise, neither is she. She dances like a duck on a treadmill.

"Come on, dance with me."

"I can't at the moment, I'm having a conversation with my new friend William about his shingles."

"You never dance with me."

"You'd assume then, based on past experience, there'd be little point asking."

"Come on, just one dance."

"The quantity of dances doesn't come into it."

"If you loved me you'd dance with me."

If you loved me, you wouldn't make me do things I don't like doing. Touché."

"That's not touché. If you loved me, you'd like doing the things you don't like doing because I like doing them and you want to please me. By doing them."

Holly loves weddings. I think it's because ours was shit and she likes to imagine she's the bride up front dressed in a beautiful white satin gown. I can't even remember what Holly was wearing at our wedding. Maybe tracksuit pants? We've talked about having a proper wedding - somewhere nice instead of a courthouse while drunk - but I only know about three people outside of work and most of Holly's friends were born in the area and haven't travelled more than half a Chevy gas tank's distance from here.

"Australia huh? I'm somewhat of a traveler myself. Just got back from Mount Jackson."

"That's a thirty-minute drive from here."

"Yes, but it's worth the trek. They have a Denny's."

Many years back, when my family lived in a small outback town in South Australia, our next-door neighbour, Mr Whitely, had a pet dingo named Dusty. You may be asking what this has to do with weddings and that's something we'll just have to discover together. I have a vague idea of how it will connect but I rarely think these things out beforehand.

"Ah, okay, I see. I like how you connected oxy-acetylene welding to Tuvan throat singing, David. That was really quite clever."
"Thank you. I planned that all along. I use Post-It notes."

Back in the 1980s, the Australian government paid a modest bounty on rabbits,* and Mr Whitely made a bit of extra beer money setting traps a few miles out of town. One evening, while checking his traps, he discovered a female dingo had been caught. According to Mr Whitely, she'd attempted to gnaw her leg off to escape, but had either bled out or died of thirst. A single dingo pup was suckling at a teat. It was tiny, barely old enough to walk, and covered in dust.

---

* *In 1859, settler Thomas Austin thought it would be good idea to introduce 13 European rabbits to Australia, as it would give him something to hunt when he ran out of Aboriginals. There's fucktillions of rabbits now, which means there's a fucktillion holes. Cows, sheep and horses break their legs regularly in the holes and if you hike anywhere, you'll step in at least fifty. Two common sentances while hiking in Australia are, "I think I've snapped another leg," and, "Are those human remains?"*

I wished, when Mr Whitely told my family the story about how he came by Dusty, he'd left out the bit about the mother trying to gnaw her leg off. It wasn't necessary to the plot and he could have just said she was dead. I thought about the dingo trying to gnaw its own leg off way too much and dreamt about it for months. Sometimes I'd dream about other animals gnawing their legs off; once it was a giraffe. I even asked my teacher how long it would take a dingo to bleed out from a leg wound - so I'd have a reference for the amount of time it had gnawed - but it was in the middle of a math class and I was told to stand outside.

"Okay, but how long?"
"Until I say you can come back inside."
"No, I mean how long before the dingo would die? Would all the blood squirt out quickly or would the dingo chew its leg for hours? How long would it take to die of thirst? It's been fairly hot lately."
"David, can you tell me what 7 x 8 is?"
"104?"

I don't do math. I've never been able to. I suppose I'm slightly mentally retarded or something, but I don't work in an industry where I need to triangulate circle trajectories or calculate the square root of houses, so I don't care.

I remember being told, "You won't always have a calculator on you," but that statement seems narrow sighted if not patently ridiculous now.

"Mrs Lawson? Remember me? David. I was in your math class in 1982."

"I'm sorry, I've taught a lot of kids over the years."

"I'm sure you have. Did you tell all of them they wouldn't always have a calculator on them?"

"Sorry?"

"Wait, let me just check my phone... It's 56, Mrs Lawson. 7 x 8 is 56. You must feel pretty fucking stupid now."

Sure, there are times when I don't have my phone on me, but I don't need to do arithmetic while I'm in the shower.

"Okay, David, if the shampoo bottle is half full and you use a squirt and a half each time you wash your hair, how long before the shampoo bottle will be empty?"

The answer is never because I add a bit of water to the bottle and shake it whenever it gets low. I've had the same bottle of shampoo since 2006. I don't think they even make it anymore.

My phone also has a calendar and a quick check tells me I have just under two months to keep Melissa's upcoming wedding a secret from Holly. I should be able to manage that. I have to. Being forced to dance is my own version of a trap I'd gnaw my leg off to escape from.

Right, maybe it wasn't the connection between wedding invitations and dusty dingoes we were all hoping for, but we established my dislike for weddings and dancing. We also learned a bit of math. That might come in useful one day if seven people ask you to get them eight items each from the supermarket. Perhaps oranges.

Also, a few years after Mr Whitely found Dusty, he had an affair with a woman named Barbara who owned Barbara's House of Hair & Fridge Magnets. Mrs Whitely found out. There was a lot of shouting and things were thrown. Mrs Whitely even went to Barbara's House of Hair & Fridge Magnets and threw things there. Probably fridge magnets. At one point, Mr Whitely slept at our house for three nights and brought Dusty with him. Dusty had free roam of our house and slept on my bed with me.

Dingoes tend to have a poor reputation in Australia, especially after one purportedly stole a baby, but apart from not barking, there's very little difference in behaviour between a dingo and your standard dog. Especially if it's been raised since a pup. Dusty chased tennis balls and watched television and tilted his head when you talked to him.

Mr Whitely went home to an emptied house. I think Mrs Whitely moved to Adelaide. I remember jumping the fence to play with Dusty and seeing only a card table and camping chair through a glass sliding door. Mrs Whitely had left Mr Whitely one thing though; a report to Wildlife Services that there was a dingo being kept as a pet on the property.

It's against the law in South Australia to have a dingo as a pet. Back then, there was a zero-tolerance policy and the animal would be seized and put down immediately.

For a few weeks, Dusty lived between Mr Whitely's house and ours. My father and Mr Whitely would pass him over the fence. When Wildlife Services checked Mr Whitely's property, he told them he had no idea what they were talking about. They went back though - while Mr Whitely wasn't home and Dusty was in the backyard.

In Australia, a lot of 4x4 vehicles have something called a 'roo bar' attached to the front. It's particularly common in rural areas. I haven't seen many in the United States apart from on a few police cars. The basic purpose of the roo bar is to stop kangaroos caving in the front or your vehicle when you hit them at speed. Mr Whitely's Land Cruiser had a roo bar and it probably helped a lot when he drove through Wildlife Services front window.

I wish I could write that he rescued Dusty and, after some kind of exciting chase with the authorities, made it over some kind of border to freedom. Or perhaps through a secret cave that led to a hidden valley. A valley where Mr Whitely lived out his days in a log cabin he built by a river, and Dusty met a girl dingo and had pups of his own.

That's not how things generally go when drive a vehicle through a government office though. Usually you receive jail time, especially if you hit a Wildlife Services officer and crush his pelvis. Mr Whitely was released on bail but shot himself in the head before his court appearance. I'm fairly certain I heard the gunshot from my bedroom. It was late and I was meant to be sleeping, but I had outfits to make for my stick people.

Update

Holly found the wedding invite. It was hidden in the kitchen junk drawer - under hundreds of used batteries, dozens of remote controls, and the manual for a popcorn maker we haven't owned since 2013 - but I forgot Holly has some kind of built-in sonar for this type of thing. She's like a bat, but instead of hunting moths, she hunts secrets.

"Oh, we're definitely going."
"But it's in a barn. With line dancing."
"That sounds like fun."
"No it doesn't. Why were you even looking in the drawer?"
"I'm allowed to look in drawers."
"Yes, but what made you think to look in there?"
"There was glitter all over the handle."

Update 2

Holly texted Melissa to thank her for the invite and they are BFFs now. They've been texting back and forth for over an hour. Apparently Scoutmaster Andrew's proposal to Melissa was very romantic; he took her camping to his favourite spot, by a river in the George Washington National Forest, and had driven to the campsite earlier that morning to set up fairy lights and a table with white linen and champagne on ice as a surprise.

I proposed to Holly while we were playing tennis and she's never let me forget it. Whenever anyone describes the romantic situation in which they were proposed to, Holly gives me a pursed lip glance. If I could go back in time, I'd at least let her win the match. It's gotten to the point where Holly actually blatantly lies about the proposal.

"And then, as Jeff and I watched the sun set in Bora Bora, the waiter brought me a piña colada and the ring was around the straw. How did David propose to you?"
"He wrote, "Holly, will you marry me?" in fireworks."
"Really?"
"Yes. And there was a band playing."
"Gosh, who?"
"The Beastie Boys."
"Oh my lord, where was it?"
"On the moon. David hired a rocket to take us all there. The fireworks people had to write, "Holly, will you marry me?" backwards because we were looking down at the Earth instead of up from it."
"You've been to the moon?"
"Yes, and the sun."

I thought tennis was appropriate because it's something Holly and I enjoy doing together. Maybe I should have had a table with white linen and champagne on ice waiting on the court, or maybe written, "Holly will you marry me?" in tennis balls. I didn't though, so there's no point harping on about it. I only had maybe six or seven tennis balls anyway. Sorry I'm not a coach.

From: Gary Wright
Date: Thursday 14 January 2021 2.16pm
To: All Staff
Subject: Friday regroup

Good afternoon,

Can we reschedule tomorrow's meeting for next week? I have someone coming to replace my Insinkerator between 10 and 12 tomorrow.

It was making a loud noise and I thought there might be a spoon in it but there wasn't and then it just stopped working. I tried pushing the button on the bottom like it says in the manual but that didn't do anything. I've only had it for 2 years. They don't make things like they used to.

Also Tim from Moen called me. There's a spelling error on the Velocity shower head packaging. It was caught on press but 12,000 units were printed with the word nuzzles instead of nozzles.

Gary

From: Mike Campbell
Date: Thursday 14 January 2021 2.38pm
To: Gary Wright. **Cc:** All Staff
Subject: Re: Friday regroup

Gary,

Are you serious? Who checked the proof? Was it Ben? We have client signoff on the artwork but they won't cover this.

Find out how much we're looking at.

How obvious is it? Could we mix the printed boxes in with a pallet of corrected ones or is it something the client will notice? Is it on the front?

Mike

....

From: Gary Wright
Date: Thursday 14 January 2021 3.02pm
To: Mike Campbell
Subject: Re: Re: Friday regroup

Mike,

It's on the back but it's quite noticeable. It's one of the dot points under the description. It says High pressure nuzzles.

Rebecca is looking at costs.

Gary

From: Mike Campbell
Date: Friday 15 January 2021 9.38am
To: David Thorne
Subject: Graphic Designer

David,

Patrick is being an asshole so I'm going into the office for a few hours. Do you want to meet for lunch at Zenebech? It's Ethiopian cuisine. They have niter kebbeh.

Bring the short list of resumes and we can discuss.

Mike

....

From: David Thorne
Date: Friday 15 January 2021 9.46am
To: Mike Campbell
Subject: Graphic Designer

Mike,

There is no short list. We've received a total of one resumé from a man named Nusrat, asking if we will fly him to the United States to work because he's, "Best graphic designer in Bangladesh."

I'll give it another week but we may have to choose between increasing the offered salary or booking Nusrat's flights. He does know how to use 'the Photoshop' as his portfolio includes the following artwork:

Walter also mentioned his friend Josh is looking for a job. I've no idea if he's any good but apparently he has a design background; they went to the same school.

What are you and Patrick arguing about?

David

From: Mike Campbell
Date: Friday 15 January 2021 9.58am
To: David Thorne
Subject: Graphic Designer

We're not arguing, Patrick is just incapable of understanding the difference between chevron and herringbone. It's like he has that mental disease where you can't see shapes.

Meet me for lunch anyway. I want to get your opinion on backsplash tiles.

Mike

....

Update: 3.05pm

I've discovered I'm not a huge fan of Ethiopian cuisine. It's a communal type of meal and I'd rather have my own plate of things. For those that haven't tried Ethiopian food, it's basically a big round bit of bread with four or five blobs of mystery meat chutneys on top. One of them may have been wasp.

While I picked at the food and played 'Which is better, this one or this one?' with 4000 backsplash tiles, Mike gave me the full story about Patrick's alleged agnosia. Apparently Patrick had referred to chevron and herringbone tiles as 'identical zigzags', and prefers penny tiles even though it isn't 2004. Mike reminded Patrick that he's a creative director, while Patrick once bought yellow bedsheets, to which Patrick responded by pouring a mug of coffee onto an egg-white portobello and zucchini breakfast omelette that had taken Mike an hour to cook.

"Chevron has 45° angles while Herringbone has 90° angles. That's a pretty big difference."

"Yes, a 45° one."

"Exactly. I love him but it's like living with a Neanderthal. Do you know what he calls Frank Lloyd Wright?"

"What?"

"Frank Wright. He says it's pretentious to use the middle name."

"No."

"Yes. And don't get me started on movies. Do you know what his favorite movie is?"

"*Pacific Rim*?"

"What? No, why would it be *Pacific Rim*? It's *Kindergarten Cop*."

"No."

"Yes. He's seen it at least fifty times and he does the, "It's not a tumor!" bit whenever anyone says the word tumor."

"The word tumor can't possibly come up in conversation that often."

"You'd be surprised. He also does it whenever anyone says 'two more'."

I'm never eating Ethiopian food again. I fell ill last night and was positive I was going to die. According to Holly, my temperature was 107°F - which means I probably have brain damage. I was in and out of consciousness and, when awake, delirious. Holly recorded some of the event to show me *A*. How severe my delirium was, and *B*. That she's basically the reincarnation of Florence Nightingale. It was a bit over the top but that's just how Holly is on camera. She's like a child in a school play who can't act, but has practiced their lines perfectly and knows to project to the audience.

"Here, take a sip. It will make you feel better, my darling."

"I can't drink seawater."

"It isn't seawater, my love, it's drinking water."

"Did you get it from a bucket?"

"No, it's from the kitchen tap. Just take a small sip... there you go."

"It tastes a bit salty."

"No, it doesn't."

"Did you check it for baby crabs?"

"Yes."

"Okay then."

JAN 2021
17
SUNDAY

Holly made a bed for me on the couch and I'm watching *Aquaman*. It's pretty bad. It has the long-haired guy from *Game of Thrones* in it and every time he appears, he raises an eyebrow and a heavy riff goes, 'Dada DUM!'. It's happened thirty-six times in the first twenty minutes of the movie and is extremely annoying.

I wouldn't have even started watching this movie if I'd known Nicole Kidman was in it. She wasn't in the trailer. She's nobody's favorite actress and her only decent role was Judy in the 1983 movie *BMX Bandits*. Wasn't she married to Tom Cruise at some point? What an idiot. She must have a thing for short men because now she's married to Keith Urban who is 3'2" and commonly mistaken for a sickly child.

"Hello, Nicole? Are you coming home soon?"
"Why, what's up, Keith? I'm kind of busy, I'm playing a fish lady that lives in a lighthouse. A-list here I come."
"I'm trapped under a kitchen sponge."
"Again?"

Honestly, why is Nicole Kidman in anything? I simply don't believe any director ever has stated, "You know who'd be perfect for this role? Nicole Kidman." Perhaps she just turns up on sets uninvited like she does at red carpet events.

"And there's Meryl Street looking absolutely gorgeous in a blue Karl Lagerfeld gown, perhaps we can g..."
"G'day!"
"Oh, it's Nicole Kidman. What a surprise."
"Yes, I'm bonza excited to be here. Keith couldn't join me this evening, because he's working on a song about dusty paddocks, but he's watching at home in Australia from his shoebox."
"Okay, so if you could just head off that wa..."
"I'm wearing Armani."
"Look, I don't mean to be rude, Nicole, but I'm really going to need you to..."
"Yes, I'm extremely excited about my latest movie role. I play Aquaman's mom."
"Wait. You're in the movie *Aquaman*? I didn't know that. You weren't in the trailer."
"It's my biggest role since penguin #28 in *Happy Feet*."

It's Tom Cruise's fault really. If he'd hired better lawyers during the divorce, Nicole wouldn't have the cash to fly to these events and bribe bouncers to let her in. She'd be doing *Celebrity Big Brother* and *Australian Dancing With the Stars* to make rent instead. How did Tom and Nicole even meet? Was it in that movie about Nascar? I bet it was.

I actually woke up feeling perfectly fine this morning, but I'm not going to let Holly know that. I like the couch bed. She's brought me several cups of tea and a cheese & pickle sandwich and I've only forgotten to look sad once when she entered the room.

"You look like you're feeling better."
"No, it was a grimace, not a smile. There's nothing to smile about in this movie, Nicole Kidman's in it. I'm feeling quite poorly and nothing will make me feel better. The cups of tea have been quite helpful though. Do we have any garlic bread?"

Update: 1.25pm

Right. I fell asleep watching *Aquaman* with my laptop open and Holly read the previous few paragraphs. It's a blatant invasion of privacy and I wish I could think of an equally unacceptable thing to do back to her. Like read her secret diary or something.

Holly doesn't have a secret diary that I know of. If she did, it wouldn't be all that interesting anyway, just page after page about how she wishes Harry Styles was her boyfriend and spinach smoothie recipes.

My couch bed is gone and Holly and I are going shopping to look for a jacket for her father.

I'm genuinely sad now.

Update: 5.36pm

We had to visit five stores to find Holly's father a jacket. One of those stores was JC Penney and Holly knows how I feel about being in there. There's no JC Penney in Australia but we have the equivalent called Harris Scarfe. It's where people buy sneakers for their least favourite child.

"Sketchers? Gavin has Nike Airs."
"Gavin also has twelve swimming trophies."

Holly's father only wears black jackets and they're not allowed to have zippers unless the zippers are also black. Not shiny black though.

"This one has black zippers. Let's just get it and go."
"They're shiny."
"All zippers are shiny."
"Some are shinier than others. We're looking for low shine zippers."
"This one has lowish shine zippers."
"Yes, but it also has elastic in the cuffs."

From: Rebecca Williams
Date: Monday 18 January 2021 11.04am
To: All Staff
Subject: Moen artwork

Morning,

I've spoken to Tim about the Moen artwork. 12,000 boxes were printed @\$1.16 which comes out to \$13,920.00.

Tim will discount 20% so final price will be \$11,136.00

Another option is to print stickers with the word nozzles to cover the word nuzzles.

12,000 stickers (24 rolls) would be \$720.00.

The shower head is a \$300 product so it's probably best to just have the boxes reprinted. We can absorb the cost and not have the client know about the mistake.

Rebecca

From: Mike Campbell
Date: Monday 18 January 2021 11.18am
To: Rebecca Williams **Cc:** All Staff
Subject: Re: Moen artwork

Rebecca,

We're not paying 11K for Ben's fuckup.

Print the stickers and have them and the boxes couriered to
Ben's house. He can spend a week sticking them on.

Maybe that'll teach him to check proofs properly.

Mike

....

From: Ben Townsend
Date: Monday 18 January 2021 11.34am
To: Mike Campbell, Jodie Smythe, David Thorne
Subject: Re: Re: Moen artwork

Mike,

I'm not sticking 12000 stickers on boxes. That will take more
than a week. Jodie should have seen the mistake when she
did the artwork.

Yes I wrote the copy and checked the proof, but David
checked my copy before it went to Jodie. If I have to stick
stickers on boxes, then so should Jodie and David.

Ben

From: Jodie Smythe
Date: Monday 18 January 2021 11.41am
To: Ben Townsend, Mike Campbell, David Thorne
Subject: Re: Re: Re: Moen artwork

Ben,

How am I meant to know they're not called high pressure nuzzles? I'm not a shower expert. I just used the copy you sent me.

Jodie

....

From: David Thorne
Date: Monday 18 January 2021 11.46am
To: Ben Townsend
Subject: Re: Re: Re: Re: Moen artwork

Ben,

I'm happy to help stick stickers on boxes.

With the two of us hammering them out it shouldn't take long. We'll call it a sticker party and order pizza and watch movies while we... no, wait, I just remembered I hate you.

David

JAN 2021

19

TUESDAY

We had an office Zoom meeting this afternoon. It was originally scheduled for 11.30 this morning, but Gary ran over someone in a Costco parking lot and Walter thought today was Saturday.

Days do tend to blur when you're working from home. There's no 9 to 5, it's just whenever to whenever with a few emails between the whenevers to give the impression you're not just binge-watching *Love on the Spectrum* on Netflix.

We've only had a few Zoom meetings since the pandemic began. They were originally intended to be weekly but the first one was just everyone fiddling with their settings and commenting on everyone's furniture, and second was cancelled ten minutes in after Melissa told Jodie her head looks big on camera, and Jodie informed Melissa that at least she wasn't a skank ho cumslut with fucked up teeth.

Jodie and Melissa have almost been fired three times due to their 'inability to conduct themselves in a professional manner,' but then they cry and say that they're best friends now and will never fight again. Last time, we had an office pool to guess how long Jodie and Melissa could keep up the 'best friends' facade. Walter was the closest with his bet of four days. He was stoked about winning until he was told he had to buy rounds at the pub with the money and said he wouldn't have bet if he'd known. Apparently he's saving up for his own Nintendo Switch because *Animal Crossing* only allows one island per console and his little sister used all the island's resources for her character on the shared family Switch. Also, she called the island Arendelle. I have no idea what any of this means and I don't care.

My bet of two weeks overestimated Jodie and Melissa's commitment and didn't take into account the fact that Melissa's 25th birthday was only three days away. Melissa's parents must have done alright for themselves because they bought Melissa a brand-new white Subaru Crosstrek for her birthday - which they could have presented to her at her apartment, but instead had it delivered to the front of our office with a giant red bow tied around it.

It was like one of those television commercials where the husband surprises his wife with a brand new Lexus in the driveway for Christmas. The ones that come on while you're watching television with your wife and you know she's thinking, 'I wish I was married to that guy' but you're fine because this year you splurged and got her a Huffy mountain bike and Rachael Ray nonstick saucepan & skillet set with bonus spatula and egg rings.

Coincidentally, Jodie also owns a Subaru Crosstrek. Hers is orange and a few years older though, with a shopping trolley ding in the passenger side door and a stained headliner from when she didn't see a speed bump while drinking a Starbuck's Frappuccino. Jodie financed her orange Crosstrek and still has two years of payments to make. Also, Melissa's Crosstrek has heated leather seats.

When people smile with genuine happiness, the voluntary contraction of the muscles that pull up the lips creates an involuntary contraction of the muscles that pull the cheekbones up, and the skin around the eyes in. It's a whole face party and the eyes are invited. Sometimes there's even a twinkle. Jodie's smile wasn't one of those smiles.

"Your parents gave you a Crosstrek for your birthday?"
"Yes."
"Oh wow."
"I know, right? I'm so happy right now."
"Me too. For you."
"First they pay off my mortgage and now this. Look, it even has personalised number plates that say MEL94."
"Yes, I see them. I considered getting personalized plates for my Crosstrek but then I decided they're a bit tacky."
"Tacky?"
"Oh, I didn't mean yours are. Just in general. I can't believe we both have the same car."
"Not really, mine's a newer model and has heated leather seats."

Generally when Melissa and Jodie have an altercation, it's difficult to ascertain who actually started the fight as there's an incremental progression from the first passing comment to raining fire. The increment count varies from fight to fight of course, based on how much shit Melissa or Jodie is prepared to put up with that day, but in this instance there weren't any increments between the heated leather seat statement and "Happy birthday slut, here's your cake."

Gary was in the foyer with Jodie and Melissa during the exchange. He didn't try to intervene though, the last time he attempted to separate the two - during a potted yucca fight over leather boots - he was elbowed in the throat and had to lie down in his office. This time, he just ran up the stairs and yelled, "Fight!" He didn't escape completely unscathed; a splatter of birthday cake struck his pants when he ran through the crossfire. He was pretty cross about it because he had a meeting to go to.

"It's completely unacceptable. I have an important meeting with Smucker's in fifteen minutes and my crotch is covered in cake icing. I tried wetting it and rubbing it off in the bathroom but if anything that made it worse. It looks like I dropped an ice cream in my lap."
"No it doesn't, Gary."
"Yes it does."
"Honestly, it doesn't."
"Are you sure?"
"Yes, it looks more like a massive cum stain."

This morning's Zoom meeting was held primarily so Mike could vent his anger about the Moen artwork, but it also covered backsplash tile finalists, Gary's chest stitches, Walter's new beard, a scathing review of *Aquaman*, and Melissa's refusal to apologise for calling Jodie fat in the last Zoom meeting.

According to Jodie, her weight is attributed to a thyroid gland problem, which is 'technically' a disability. Further, discriminating against someone because of their disability is not only rude, it's a fireable offence. Melissa countered that 'technically' she didn't call Jodie fat, she'd just pointed out that, "Some guys like fat girls," so Jodie can "fuck right off." Jodie's response was to give the finger, ask, "Stolen anything from Sephora lately?", then log off before Melissa could respond.

Every fat person I've ever known has said they have a thyroid problem, not a cake problem, so I don't know. It seems easy to blame your thyroid when it can't defend itself against the allegation.

"I have a thyroid problem."
"Oh fuck off, Jodie, don't blame me. You ate fifteen pancakes at iHop this morning. I'm doing the best I can under difficult circumstances."

I'm also not sure why fat people act so astonished when people call them fat. Do they not own mirrors?

"Do these pants make me look fat?"

"No, of course not, it's your calorie intake and inactivity."

"Oh lordy, help me, I'm being attacked."

Someone who should definitely look in a mirror and be honest with himself is Walter. His beard looks like he skinned an elderly dog with mange and glued it to his face. I informed Walter of this and he stated, "You're just jealous because you can't grow a beard." Which isn't true, I just have no desire to look homeless. I'm going more for the aging goth in denial look.

Another topic raised during today's Zoom meeting was the lack of applicants for the design position. Mike is positive it has nothing to do with the salary of three beans and a piece of string being offered, and stated, "People just don't want to work at the moment."

I don't want to work any of the moments. I only do it for the money. If I were rich, I wouldn't wake up in the morning and think to myself, 'Hmm, might spend the day adding gleams to a photo of a toaster.'

I saw an interview a few years back with a guy who won 300 million dollars playing the lottery. When the reporter asked, "How will this change your life?", the guy replied, "It won't really, I'm still going to go to work Monday morning."

Please. The only logical reason to go to work Monday

morning would be to see your coworker's expressions when you arrive by solid gold helicopter.

"Well I should be off, just dropped by to say fuck you, it's been horrible, and I hate you all. Have fun being poor."

"Um, we're going to need two weeks notice, Bob."

Surprisingly, we did receive another resumé today. It's from a woman named Edith who, despite being 74, assures us she's very mobile and her daughters have a problem keeping up with her. While she has no experience in the design industry, she's a very quick learner and owns her own laptop. She's currently top of the list.

Seb doesn't have to work today so he's agreed to let me cut his hair. I'm rather surprised by this as the last time I cut it, when he was seven, it came out looking worse than Walter's beard. Maybe he's forgotten or has blocked the memory; I know he was teased at school for a few weeks. I used an electric bread knife.

He also let me pierce his ear once. Begged me to really. Seb's best friend at school, Brian, had his ear pierced a few days earlier, and a girl in class said it was cool. We numbed Seb's ear with ice, positioned his head on the kitchen chopping board, and I hammered a nail through his lobe. It worked, but the nail went into the chopping board and I had to use the claw side of the hammer to pry it out. There was a lot of screaming and Seb changed his mind about wanting his ear pierced.

Update

It's an established fact that the only difference between a bad haircut and a good haircut is two weeks. Seb needs to accept this and apologise for chasing me with scissors.

JAN   2021

21
THURSDAY

Melissa sent us all a list of presents she wants this morning. I get that wedding registries are a thing but they usually include affordable items such as glassware and bathrobes, maybe a Keurig machine or knife block set. The cheapest item on Melissa's list is a Breville Bambino Plus Espresso Machine for $499.95

Bitch is getting a toaster. It's not going to be a Breville one either, we're talking Hamilton Beach.

Apparently we're also now meant to dress for the event - like extras in a western themed musical - in cowboy hats, boots, jeans, and bandanas instead of masks. None of this was disclosed earlier and I'm not impressed. I don't own any of these items, not even jeans; I find them uncomfortable and kind of seventies, like something Farah Fawcett might wear to a picnic.

Holly owns about four thousand pairs of jeans. That's just an estimate of course, there could be a few thousand more. They're organised by colour, shade, thickness, style, and date.

I know this because whenever Holly states she has no jeans to wear and I offer suggestions, her response is always one of the following:

"Oh my god, you're not helpful at all. That's the black jeans section. Why the fuck would I wear black jeans to a birthday party?"

"Really? Light blue jeans with a white shirt? It's not the eighties, David. Just go away if you're going to be stupid about it."

"It's summer. I'll cook in those. Why did I even ask you?"

"Yeah right, like I'm going to wear capris with these shoes. That does it, I'm not going."

"Is that meant to be a joke? I haven't worn those jeans since 1998. I hate you and wish you were dead."

Okay, that last one was an exaggeration but not a huge one. It's not as if Holly does any better selecting outfits for me either. A few years back, I set fire to myself by accident, and the hospital cut off my clothes. When I was released from the hospital, Holly picked me up and brought me an outfit to wear home. I had to walk through the hospital, down an elevator, and into the parking lot wearing a pair of *Rick & Morty* pajama shorts and a t-shirt way too small for me. The shirt was one of Seb's and had the word Minecraft written across the front in block letters, with some kind of cube person underneath.

From: Ben Townsend
Date: Friday 22 January 2021 10.16am
To: All staff
Subject: No subject

Seriously, this is bullshit.

Ben

JAN 2021
23
SATURDAY

My fingers are all crampy and probably have permanent damage. I was thinking about learning the piano but that's not happening now. I had no intention of helping Ben with the stickers, but then Walter offered to help and I felt bad for not checking the proof properly... also, Walter always has marijuana on him and I've been out for months.

Marijuana is legal in DC, you can get it anywhere. There are even delivery services. Technically, the marijuana can't be sold, but due to some kind of legal loophole, it can be gifted. This means you buy a pair of socks, for example, and the socks come with a free jar of buds. It's stupid, everyone knows it's stupid, but that's just the way it is. One of the delivery services actually offers legal advice with a free gift.

knock knock
"Hello."
"Hello. In Virginia, it's illegal to hunt or kill any bird or animal, including nuisance species, on Sundays. However, it is permissible to kill raccoons."
"I did not know that. Here's your fifty dollars."
"Thank you. And here's your free Purple Kush."

I'm not a huge marijuana smoker. I used to be, but one afternoon, after realising I'd been staring at a roll of paper towels for an hour, I decided it might be time to cut back a little. I won't smoke around other people, as stoned people are boring, but if I'm alone and I don't have anything important to do, I do still enjoy the occasional shower smoke.

"Would you like a toke, David?"
"No thank you, I only smoke marijuana in the shower."
"That's a thing?"
"Yes."

We all have our things. Some people get stoned to watch movies or do the vacuuming, I prefer to be wet and warm. Not much happens during shower smokes, it's not a quick scrub and hop out process, I just let the hot water run over my head for an hour or so. It's almost spiritual in a way and certainly cleansing.

Walter smokes a lot. He's one of those people who knows the difference between sativa and indica strains, where they're grown, and the THC percentage. He also never has just one type of marijuana, but rather a selection to suit different activities. That's why I buy through him.

"Shower smoke? Relaxing or thinking?"
"Thinking."
"Rainbow Sprinkles. I'll bring some to Ben's for you. It's a gift but I'll need fifty dollars for the sandwich bag."

Ben had a kind of factory line system set up in his living room when I arrived. He was concerned that the weight of all the boxes might collapse the floor, so it was a five box at a time system. Each box contained approximately three hundred die-cut unassembled shower head boxes which had to be taken out, have a sticker applied, then put back in a box. Which doesn't sound like it would take that long.

"My arms are killing, how many have we done?"

"Almost half a box."

"Oh my god. When is Walter getting here to help?"

"He should be here soon. His friend Josh offered to help so Walter is picking him up on the way."

"Why wasn't I informed of this?"

"What does it matter?"

"I would have dressed differently if I'd known I was meeting someone new. I'm wearing tracksuit pants and a Duran Duran t-shirt."

"I wouldn't have pegged you as a Duran Duran fan actually."

"I'm not."

"Then why are you wearing a Duran Duran shirt?"

"Because it's soft and comfortable. And because I thought it was only going to be the three of us. I don't give a fuck what you and Walter think."

"I'm wearing track pants as well."

"Nobody cares what you wear, it's your house. Josh is going to assume this is how I normally dress to leave my house. First impressions count."

"That's true. I might change actually."

I *am* a Duran Duran fan. Definitely more of a closet fan than an openly proud one though, and it comes and goes in phases. I'm one of those fans that hates the better-known singles and prefers the album tracks, but only one or two from each album. Like *The Chauffeur* from the album *Rio* or *Ordinary World* from *The Wedding Album*. If you aren't familiar with those tracks, it doesn't matter, they're not particularly groundbreaking. Sometimes songs just insert themselves into a section of our brains, like a sticky note or bookmark, to flag a past moment in our lives.

Duran Duran was the first band I ever saw in concert. The ticket cost $13.50 and my cousin Neil took me. Neil also dressed me; I wore a yellow t-shirt with slashes cut in it and a green Slazenger headband. Neil wore black leather pants with a white puffy shirt. He was pretty much a super fan and had the hair and the 12" remix cassingles and had watched the *Planet Earth* music video hundreds of times to perfect Simon LeBon's dance moves.* After the concert, I sat in the front seat of his car while he had sex in the back with a girl dressed as Madonna. I was eleven.

Once the grunting and slapping was over, Neil and the Madonna lookalike shared a 'weird smelling cigarette' with all the windows rolled up while we listened to *Rio*. They essentially hotboxed an eleven-year-old.

---

* *Skipping on the spot while waving invisible semaphore flags.*

"I saw you look in the rear vision mirror."

"No I didn't, I was looking at the moon. What's this song?"

"*The Chauffeur*. Fast forward it."

"No, I like it. I should buy leather pants. How much did yours cost?"

Neil paid two hundred dollars for his leather pants, which is kind of excessive. A few years later, I received a box of hand-me-down clothes from him and the leather pants were in there. He'd moved on from Duran Duran by then and gained a few pounds. I wore the leather pants to school once but they were squeaky and hot and almost impossible to ride my bike in.

Neil died in a gyrocopter crash in 2003. It was one of those kit gyrocopters that you buy the plans for and build yourself. He clipped a powerline on his maiden flight and burst into flames. It made the local news and the manager of the Kuralta Park Kmart was interviewed about the crash - she said the store had been without power for several hours and that the pilot didn't have permission to use their parking lot as an airstrip. I hadn't kept in contact with Neil but I played the album *Rio* after I learned he died. Some of it at least. A couple of tracks.

Ben and I had completed almost a whole box by the time Walter and Josh arrived. It would have been more but Ben changed his outfit three times before finally settling on some weird beige ensemble.

"Crikey."

"Is that good or bad in Australian?"

"It's Steve Irwin's catchphrase."

"That's not a catchphrase. It's a word. A catchphrase is a sentence."

"The autistic guy on *The Big Bang Theory* has Bazinga! as his catchphrase."

"That's different. It has an exclamation point so technically it's classed as a one-word sentence. Like Ahoy!"

"Crikey!"

"What's your point?"

"You're dressed like Steve Irwin."

"No I'm not, Steve Irwin wore khakis. This is a safari suit."

Generally when someone mentions a friend I haven't met, I automatically assume that friend must kind of look like the person telling me about them - if someone with long hair, for example, wears death metal band t-shirts, I assume the people they hang out with also dress like poor people. Walter is a cargo shorts and sneakers kind of guy, mid-twenties, skinny with a mop of hair like an inverted bird's nest.

Josh was easily forty, dressed in a shiny grey suit, and very overweight. He looked bloated, like a body fished out of a river - the effect amplified by his suit being at least three sizes too small. His trousers were so tight it looked as though he'd shoved a bumpy potato down the front, and he walked without bending his knees. He *was* wearing a mask though, so he gets points for that.

"Nice to meet you, Josh. Would you prefer to sit or be propped at a 60° angle against the wall?"

"What?"

"It was a snide but lighthearted comment regarding your suit. It's very tight."

"Yeah, I haven't worn it for a while and I gained a few pounds during the pandemic. I need to cut back on the burgers."

"Well at least you don't blame your thyroid gland. Why are you wearing a suit to apply stickers to boxes?"

"I wanted to make a good impression."

"Right, well I feel bad about the 60° angle comment now. I was pretty pleased with it at the time. Walter tells me you're a designer."

"Yeah. I was going to apply for the job at your agency but the salary is kind of low."

"Yes, it is."

"Duran Duran fan?"

"Intermittently."

"Favourite song?"

"Probably *The Chauffeur*."

"Nice. Mine's *Ordinary World*."

"Right, well you can come and sit by me, Josh."

JAN 2021

24

SUNDAY

Mike, just so you're aware. I may have offered Walter's friend Josh the design position yesterday. He helped put on stickers at Ben's.

You may have? What does that mean?

I was tired and stoned.

I thought you only smoke in the shower?

Usually, but by sticker 3000 of 12000, I thought, 'the only way I'm going to survive this is to disconnect somehow.' Ben made us watch the Lord of the Rings movies. All of them. I think there was like fifteen.

Okay. As long as he knows what he's doing. Decent portfolio?

JAN 2021

25

MONDAY

I should have asked to see Josh's portfolio before offering him the position. I definitely should have checked with Mike before offering 45K. There's a saying about never promising to do something when you're in a good mood. There should also be a saying about offering people positions when you can't feel your arms or face and you're deliriously tired and you're being forced to watch movies about magic.

"Who's that guy? Is he magic as well?"
"That's Bilbo. Have you been watching the movie at all?"
"Oh, he looks different with wet hair."

I don't like movies about magic. I don't care if it's magic rings or magic schoolkids, they're all pointless and have the same ending. You may as well just fast-forward to the 'and then he/she/they did magic and won' bit every time.

That's how I'm going to end this book actually, just so you can see how pointless and annoying it is. You're welcome to skip to the end and check. Make sure you come back and read the rest though, because there's stuff about the power of friendship and maybe dragon eggs.

From: David Thorne
Date: Monday 25 January 2021 9.44am
To: Walter Bowers
Subject: Josh

Walter,

Can you send me Josh's contact details please? And a link to his portfolio. Thanks.

David

....

From: Walter Bowers
Date: Monday 25 January 2021 10.26am
To: David Thorne
Subject: Re: Josh

What portfolio his furniture He hasnt but you can if you facebook. He made the barrel table at my house.

....

From: David Thorne
Date: Monday 25 January 2021 10.31am
To: Walter Bowers
Subject: Re: Re: Josh

Walter,

I can what if I Facebook? I shouldn't need to fly in Amy Adams to decipher your attempts at communication.

If Josh doesn't have a portfolio online, please ask him to send me a pdf. And his resume.

David

....

From: Walter Bowers
Date: Monday 25 January 2021 10.49am
To: David Thorne
Subject: Re: Re: Re: Josh

You can if you GO ONTO facebook.

He doesnt have a portfolio he does more furniture design. He knows illustrator and photoshop though and hes really good with 3D software I think he uses blender

....

From: David Thorne
Date: Monday 25 January 2021 10.53am
To: Walter Bowers
Subject: Re: Re: Re: Re: Josh

Walter,

That will be certainly come in handy if we decide to pitch for the next installment of *Toy Story*. You said he went to the same school as you.

David

From: Walter Bowers
Date: Monday 25 January 2021 11.01am
To: David Thorne
Subject: Re: Re: Re: Re: Re: Josh

The same high school

....

From: David Thorne
Date: Monday 25 January 2021 11.09am
To: Walter Bowers
Subject: Re: Re: Re: Re: Re: Re: Josh

Right.

I'm blaming you entirely for this Walter.

Do not mention to Mike that Josh made your barrel table.

David

....

From: Walter Bowers
Date: Monday 25 January 2021 11.16am
To: David Thorne
Subject: Re: Re: Re: Re: Re: Re: Re: Josh

Why not its cool

From: David Thorne
Date: Monday 25 January 2021 11.21am
To: Walter Bowers
Subject: Re: Re: Re: Re: Re: Re: Re: Re: Josh

Is it though? It's a barrel with a piece of round glass on top.

David

....

From: Walter Bowers
Date: Monday 25 January 2021 11.32am
To: David Thorne
Subject: Re: Re: Re: Re: Re: Re: Re: Re: Re: Josh

No its also got a door in it with hinges Theres a shelf inside.

JAN 2021

26

TUESDAY

It took Walter less than one day to inform Mike that Josh made his barrel table. I don't know how that even comes up in normal conversation. Mike called me and I explained how I feel about movies about magic, which turned into a bit of a shouting match about checking proofs and professionalism. Mike hung up on me then rang back a short time later to apologise for hanging up on me, reiterate his views on barrel tables, and hang up on me again.

Often during a heated altercation, it's best to simply state, "You're right, I made a mistake, and I apologise." For some reason though, that's a lot harder than listing several examples of why the other person has no right to call you a 'fucking cabbage' when they themselves have clearly demonstrated cabbageness in the past.

"And that's just eighteen examples. I have another thirty or so if you'd like to hear them."
"Sure."
"Okay, example nineteen; during a client meeting in 2016, you asked if cows give birth or lay eggs."
"Do I look like a farmer?"

After a string of text messages, another apology, and a group FaceTime call with Walter to establish a clearer timeline of events, it was decided we should give Josh the two-week trial he was promised. I don't think I did actually promise anything, but Walter seems to think otherwise and called me, "An Indian giver. But with jobs."

It was also decided that none of this would have happened if we had an HR manager. Mike stated he will have the job description written by the end of the week. Next week at the latest. So maybe mid-August.

Josh will be attending the regroup this Friday to meet everyone. In the meantime, Jodie is sending him artwork we did last year for a client's annual report. This year's redesign of the annual report won't be due for a few months, but it will give us a chance to determine Josh's abilities.

Also, Gary received his first Covid-19 vaccination today. He's pretty proud of the fact and posted a photo of his vaccination record on Facebook. It has his birthdate on it (1955) so I know he lied about turning 59 last year. Apparently, Gary was able to get the vaccine early because of his age and the fact that he has a stent in his heart. I wasn't aware he had heart issues and there's been several times I've hidden behind doors and scared him. I don't yell 'Boo!' or anything, I just whisper, "Gary," and he screams and then I chuckle for several minutes. I should probably stop that.

JAN **2021**

27
WEDNESDAY

From: David Thorne
Date: Wednesday 27 January 2021 9.52am
To: Gary Wright
Subject: Lovells meeting

Gary,

Hope you are feeling well after your shot. Jodie and I have a meeting with Joseph Lovells tomorrow regarding changes to their stationery. Do you want to be in that meeting? If so, why?

David

....

From: Gary Wright
Date: Wednesday 27 January 2021 10.16am
To: David Thorne
Subject: Re: Lovells meeting

No, I don't need to be there. Why is your text so big?

Gary

From: David Thorne
Date: Wednesday 27 January 2021 10.22am
To: Gary Wright
Subject: Re: Re: Lovells meeting

Gary,

It's 'larger print for older readers'. The photo you posted yesterday of your vaccination card shows your birthdate.

I've always said you look rough for your age. Were you called upon to do your part by buying war bonds?

David

....

From: Gary Wright
Date: Wednesday 27 January 2021 10.31am
To: David Thorne
Subject: Re: Re: Re: Lovells meeting

I'm not in the mood for your bullshit today.

I can't help it if the woman who signed my vaccination card wrote the wrong date. The people who organize these things should check their volunteers aren't illiterate.

Gary

JAN 2021

28

THURSDAY

It was strange putting on a suit and tie this morning. I felt like an actor donning a costume before going on stage, or an astronaut sealing his spacesuit before stepping out into an alien landscape.

"That's one small step for man, one slightly larger typesize for letterheads."

It must be nice having a job that matters, like being a doctor without fences or a mattress salesman; you can't overvalue the benefits of a good night's sleep.

Contribution to society-wise, graphic designers are only one step up from hairdressers and one step down from department store mannequin. People say that it's never too late to change careers - which might be true of other fields - but being a graphic designer is kind of like being a spy or an assassin; you don't get to leave or retire, you just become an older graphic designer. Some try to escape, but other graphic designers are sent after them with nice grids or a clever logotype to bring them back in to the fold.

"Worked on any nice design projects lately, Dennis?"

"No, I haven't done any graphic design in years. I hate design, I hate other designers, and I hate everything about the industry. I managed to escape and I'm finally happy."

"Nice. What do you think about this logotype?"

"Hmm. Kerning could do with a little work. The spacing between the D and O in particular needs to be tighter but I like the balance between the... goddamnit."

Jodie picked me up early this morning. I would have preferred to drive separately but I didn't say so because I have excellent social skills.

"Should we take my car instead, Jodie?"

"Why?"

"Because it's bigger and doesn't smell like cat urine."

Jodie drives a Subaru Crosstrek which is like a reverse TARDIS in that it's a lot smaller on the inside than you'd think possible. There's only about four square feet of interior space, which might be plenty for anorexic dwarves, but anyone else needs to be okay with touching shoulders and holding their head at 90°. I've been in boxes that are bigger.

"I feel like Alice after she ate the cake and grew inordinately large. Does this seat go back any further?"

"No, it's as far back as it goes."

"How much oxygen do you think we have in here? Enough for the whole trip?"

Everyone who works in the design industry has their favourite clients - the ones that have a lot of money, leave you alone, and are ecstatic with whatever you come up with - and clients you'd happily shoot in the neck with a crossbow if there was some kind of purge and you wouldn't be prosecuted. The crossbow clients are the ones that have thirty changes they'd like to see based on feedback from their wife's sister's ferret, prefer to meet in person, and don't understand why they're being charged for simple changes to all the text, images, and layout.

Figure A. *Favourite client project timeline*

Figure B. *Crossbow client project timeline*

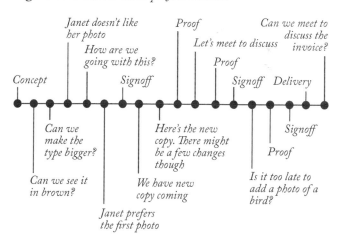

Really, there should be about fifty more black circles in figure B, but I ran out of room. Even staggering the text to fit was a nightmare and I considered scrapping the whole thing about ten minutes in. You wouldn't have known. I could have filled the blank space with the photo of a bird. Maybe a seagull. In one of my previous books, I replaced a whole page of text with a photo of a fish. I used it as part of my marketing by stating 'Now with bonus photo of a fish.'

I've never been good at marketing; when I do have to promote my books, I feel like one of those old guys you see holding Little Caesar's Pizza signs on main roads.

"And what do you want to be when you grow up, Robert?"
"A pole."

There's only one reason Jodie and I were required to attend the client meeting in person today, and it's not because the information couldn't be provided by single paragraph email, it's because some clients are so incredibly dull, a captive audience is their only chance at social interaction.

"Please, Mr Lovells, just let us go. We don't care that your company's history includes a move from 320 Dawson Street to 354 Dawson Street in 1976. We get that you're lonely but none of this information is relevant to your pamphlet about earwax buildup."
"Shhh. Keep dancing. Now, where was I? Oh yes, I had a moustache back then, as was the fashion..."

The worst part about today's pointless meeting wasn't the client's two-hour expedition through the history of aural hygiene, or his office that smelled like mold and sadness, it was the ride there and back with Jodie. We have little in common, apart from working in the same industry, and it was a 45-minute drive both ways. This meant 90 minutes of Jodie bitching about Melissa, and an entire Adele album.

"And that's another reason why Melissa can't be trusted; her mom is a Mormon. You can't really be serious about going to her wedding?"
"Yes, I'm looking forward to it. Big fan of barns. Can we listen to something else?"
"Like what?"
"Something that isn't dreadful."
"Adele isn't dreadful. She's amazing."
"Is she though? It's elevator music for middle-aged women shopping in Macy's. Sure, she can sing, but the songs are self-absorbed wank. I must have called a thousand times? Okay, well that's stalking, Adele. Time to move on. Sorry, but he's obviously just not into big girls."
"Well I like her."
"Of course you do. It's the musical equivalent of chips."

The biggest problem I have with Adele isn't actually her music - I get that there's a market for her stuff just as there's a market for beige velour sofas - it's her album covers. Who wants to see her huge head on every single one of them? She does, that's who.

JAN   2021
29
FRIDAY

I would have bet a month's salary that Mike wouldn't have the HR job description written by today. I would have lost and Holly would have yelled at me for being so irresponsible with money. Maybe had an affair. I'd be understanding but not forgiving and move into a small apartment. Or maybe a cabin in the woods. I could have a pet raccoon.

We're advertising the HR position on Monday. We will also be advertising for a new graphic designer, as even Walter was shocked by Josh's annual report presentation during this morning's 'regroup'. I put the ' things around the word regroup because there were only four of us; Mike, myself, Josh and Walter. Jodie and Melissa are refusing to be in the same room as each other, Rebecca is self-isolating after a member of her book club* tested positive for Covid, and Gary is taking a PTO day to take his mother shopping for a dehumidifier.

---

* *Rebecca once recommended one of my books for her book club. I won't say which one as it received a group score of 4/10 and was described as 'pointless, poorly written, and discriminatory against large women.'*

Years ago, during the eighties, I was a big fan of the magazine *Smash Hits*. It was pop music based, featuring bios and interviews with the likes of Nik Kershaw, Tears For Fears, and The Thompson Twins, and came with a pull-out poster. The cover reflected the design of the time; neon colours and zigzags, maybe a couple of spirals chucked in for good measure. Sometimes it had red writing on a blue background and if you wiggled it, it looked like the text was moving.

Josh's annual report design - printed and mounted on presentation boards like we used to do in the nineties - looked like a copy of *Smash Hits*. There was no grid structure, no negative space, no contrast and harmony, no kerning. There are fundamental design principles that even first year design students are indoctrinated with; these principles can be stretched and played with if you know what you're doing, but to design something that is completely devoid of even one of these principles takes effort. Which is why I initially thought Josh's design was an elaborate joke - that he was waiting to see our reaction before stating, "Lol, just kidding, here's the real design."

"That's brilliant, Josh. Look at Mike's face. Hahaha."

Nobody else laughed and there was no reveal of the 'real' design. Mike simply got up and walked out. He held eye contact with me, showing no emotion, as he closed the boardroom door behind him. Walter shook his head and said, "Wow, Josh, that's shit."

From: David Thorne
Date: Friday 29 January 2021 1.26pm
To: Josh Argobast
Subject: Position

Hello Josh,

We can probably agree this morning's presentation didn't go quite as well as we all would have liked. I should have explained the role expectations in detail prior to offering you the position and I apologise for not doing so.

Regardless, Mike and I feel it may be best at this point to cut your two-week trial short. You will still be paid for the full two weeks. Melissa will be in contact with you Monday.

All the best with your future endeavors etc.

Regards, David

....

From: Josh Argobast
Date: Friday 29 January 2021 1.48pm
To: David Thorne
Subject: Re: Position

David,

I just think I should be allowed to redo the design. I was going for a retro design but I can do normal stuff as well. I'm very adaptive.

Josh

From: David Thorne
Date: Friday 29 January 2021 2.02pm
To: Josh Argobast
Subject: Re: Re: Position

Josh,

I appreciate that but there are fundamental design principles that need to be understood before any design is undertaken; regardless of whether it's retro or 'normal'. We need someone who lives and breathes grids and typefaces.

If you're serious about pursuing a career in graphic design, I'd suggest getting a hold of *Grid Systems* by Josef Müller-Brockmann and *Principles of Two-Dimensional Design* by Wucius Wong. And for reference material, the *LogoLounge* series - all of them.

Walter will also have his own suggestions. He's an excellent designer and a good resource to have.

Regards, David

....

From: Josh Argobast
Date: Friday 29 January 2021 2.13pm
To: David Thorne
Subject: Re: Re: Re: Position

I don't need your suggestions. I've been a designer for longer than Walter has.

There's no difference between designing furniture or annual reports. They follow the same rules.

You're not as special as you think you are. Sorry but your just not. Your loss.

Josh

....

From: David Thorne
Date: Friday 29 January 2021 2.22pm
To: Josh Argobast
Subject: Re: Re: Re: Re: Position

Josh,

You're correct, but there *is* a difference between Herman Miller furniture and slapping a piece of glass on top of a barrel.

Again, I apologise for not sufficiently explaining the role requirements and I take full responsibility for wasting your time. It might be suggested a portion of accountability could be attributed to your assumption the position doesn't require a specific skillset, but suggestions aren't welcome around here.

Best of luck with your furniture design. I'm sure there's a huge untapped market for broom & bucket hatstands and shipping pallet beds.

Regards, David

From: Josh Argobast
Date: Friday 29 January 2021 2.35pm
To: David Thorne
Subject: Re: Re: Re: Re: Re: Position

Eat a dick.

....

From: David Thorne
Date: Friday 29 January 2021 2.37pm
To: Josh Argobast
Subject: Re: Re: Re: Re: Re: Re: Position

Josh,

I've accepted my role as the bad guy in this situation and expected animosity, but what does 'eat a dick' even mean? Are you implying an act of submission or pleasure?

David

....

From: Josh Argobast
Date: Friday 29 January 2021 2.44pm
To: David Thorne
Subject: Re: Re: Re: Re: Re: Re: Re: Position

Look it up in one of your books.

JAN   2021

30

SATURDAY

I learned this morning that my mother died a few months ago. Her name was Diane. I'm not sure how I'm meant to feel about her death, as we weren't close. Writing '*was* Diane' instead of '*is*' caused me to pause for a moment, but it was a brief moment. I've felt more emotion watching television commercials for St. Jude's Children's Hospital even though I've worked in advertising and know exactly how it all works.

"Can we swap this child for a more attractive one please? Preferably one that's able to smile on cue despite the pain."
"How about this one?"
"No, she's not bald enough. And she's Mexican. Nobody in America wants to see Mexican kids getting free cancer treatment. We might stick a black kid in somewhere for legal reasons, but only one and it has to be from a talent agency. We can shave its head if we need to, it's in their contract."
"What about this one? He's white, completely bald, and the pain from eighteen bone marrow transplants has contorted his face into a permanent smile."
"Fine, he'll do. Just stick a few more tubes up his nose and give him a colouring book. I don't want to be here all day, it's fucking depressing."

A death in the family does tend to make you think about your own mortality though. That and accidently looking at the X10 side of a bathroom magnifying mirror. I looked at the magnified side of one the other day while shopping in Bed Bath & Beyond with Holly, and I've decided I'm never standing within twenty feet of anyone ever again.

Before that moment, I believed I looked 'somewhere in my early forties' but the magnified mirror informed me I could pass for Walter Matthau's dad. It also let me know that there was a thick black hair, approximately a centimetre long, growing out of one of the manhole sized pores in my nose.

"Holly, there's a thick black hair growing out of my nose. Did you know that?"
"Yes, it's hard to miss."
"What? How long has it been there?"
"I don't know, six months."
"And you didn't think to mention it?"
"I figured you'd seen it."
"And what, I decided to keep it? To see how long it would get? Why would I do that?"
"Who knows why you do half the things you do."

Along with, "Looks good, let's go," and, "Will you rub my back?", the phrase, "Who knows why you do half the things you do," is an integral multi-use tool in Holly's repertoire. It serves as dismissal, insult, justification, and accusation reinforcement.

"Where's the measuring cup gone? Have you seen it?"

"No, Holly."

"Did you throw it out?"

"Why would I throw out the measuring cup?"

"Who knows why you do half the things your do."

"That's just your go-to response when you have no basis for the accusation."

"Past behaviour is the basis. You threw out the wooden Christmas nativity my parents gave us last year."

"Yes, because we're atheists. Why the fuck would we want a wooden nativity scene in our house? It's as if your parents purposely seek out the tackiest rubbish they can find at Dollar General in an effort to fuck with our interior design choices and turn our house into Grandma Bumpkin's trailer in the woods. They gave us a ceramic statue of a bear with a butterfly on its nose the year before. I threw that out as well. And the tassled sofa pillow with Nascar driver Dale Earnhardt Jr.'s face on it."

"They mean well."

"I'm sure they do. They probably thought, 'You know what would go well with David and Holly's mid-century modern furniture? A Nascar pillow. Neither of them have the slightest interest in Nascar but everyone loves tassels.' The next time they give us something dreadful, I'm just going to say, 'No, sorry, that's not going in our house, it's hideous and I hate it.'"

"Why would you do that?"

"Who knows why I do half the things I do, Holly."

"You weren't hugged much as a child, were you?"

I ran away from home when I was five. I didn't like being there and I knew of a much better house where lots of kids lived - a couple of the kids were around my age. I wasn't sure of the address but I knew what the front of the house looked like because I'd seen it dozens of times. Our house was a place where you had to be quiet and weren't allowed to touch anything. A house of good behaviour. The house I was running away to was full of life and laughter - there was a seesaw in the backyard and the family did fun activities together, such as sack racing. I knew there was a spare bed for me in Peter and Bobby's room because Greg, the oldest brother, had recently moved into the attic.

I only made it four or five blocks before Mr Kostas, our Greek neighbour, drove past and stopped to ask where I was off to and if I wanted a lift. Apparently he didn't watch a lot of television because we drove around for half an hour or so looking for the Brady house before he took me home. Or perhaps he was just humouring me. We did stop to pick up several bags of concrete and some rebar from a hardware store on the way and he told me a story about how his mother used to whip him with an olive tree branch when he got poor grades at school.

I assume there was a funeral for Diane, I wasn't told. Probably because whoever arranged it, most likely my sister Leith, knew I wouldn't attend. Or she didn't want to split the proceeds from the sale of Diane's house. I don't care. She needs the money more than I do. It can't be easy raising five kids from five different fathers who are all either in prison or gave false names and addresses and can't be located.

"Who's my dad?"
"Lamp Couch Hallway. He had brown hair just like yours."
"Will I ever meet him?"
"No, he's an astronaut and lives on the moon. Hush now, finish your 1/5th of the Big Mac then get ready for bed. It's your turn to have the blanket tonight."
"Yay!"

I once lent my sister five hundred dollars, to fix the transmission on her van, and she bought an above ground pool. I never saw a cent of the money again and I never went for a swim because, well, it was an above ground pool. Even if you build a deck around one everyone knows what it is. Nobody says, "Oh really? It's an above ground pool? You'd never be able to tell." They say, "Oh, the invite didn't mention it's an above ground pool. I wouldn't have come if I'd known." Maybe not to your face but that's what they're saying. Leith didn't have a deck around her pool so everyone just sat in Coleman camping chairs looking up at it. I mentioned the money a few years later and Leith stated, "I bought you a pool float."

I don't even know how Diane died. She was only in her sixties and did Pilates so maybe it was an illness or an automobile accident. I hope it was quick because in the end, that's all any of us can hope for. A quick death, sometime in my seventies, is basically my retirement plan. I don't care how I die as long as it's quick and has nothing to do with sharks. I know a guy named Jason that used to work as an EMT and he told me that a surprisingly large amount of people die on the toilet. Apparently pushing out a big poo puts the cardiovascular system at risk by raising blood pressure, increasing the risk of a stroke or heart attack. I'm at that age where I can have a stroke or drop dead at any time so I always make sure my hair is done and I'm wearing clean underwear before I take a dump. I also cover my genitals with a towel and make sure my browser history has been deleted.

Apparently Diane was quite good looking when she was young but I've seen photos of her in a marriage album and I never thought so. Perhaps because she wasn't smiling in any of them. I saw Diane smile three times when I was growing up. I'm sure she smiled more often than that and I've just forgotten, but that's all I can recall. Once was when Gravox sent her two pallets of tins of instant gravy after she cut her thumb on a lid and wrote them a scathing letter, once during the telecast of Prince Charles and Lady Diana's wedding, and once when my father fell out of a boat. The boat was on a trailer and my father broke his arm.

All three smiles occurred before my father left. It's possible she smiled when I was a baby but I don't remember much before the age of five so I have no idea when she realized she never should have married my father and had children.

Diane wasn't a terrible mother, she went through the motions, but it was a fairly transparent performance in a role that brought her no joy. It was the 'movie adaption of a book' version of motherhood that omitted certain dialogue and character development in order to fit within the ninety-minute runtime audiences are comfortable with. But made for television. On a budget. With an actor you know you've seen in something else but can't quite put your finger on it. It might have been that show about rescue helicopter pilots.

I was eleven when I had my first sleepover at a friend's house. I know that's old to be having your first sleepover but my mother didn't like other kids at our house because we had an expensive rug or something, I think it was Berber, and sleeping at other kid's houses involved being dropped off and picked up and the possibility of her having to talk to other parents. It was a lot of work.

"Mum, can I sleep over Michael's house?"
"Who's Michael Wilson?"
"My best friend from school. You don't have to do anything."
"Have I met Michael?"
"Not yet."
"Then no. What would people think? For all I know his father might be a child rapist."
"He's not. He's a washing machine mechanic."
"Definitely not then. Are they poor?"
"No. They have a pool."
"Above ground or inground?"

Michael and I had pizza for dinner and played *Missile Command* on his Atari until his mother told us to go to sleep for the fourth or fifth time. Before Michael's mother turned out the light, she held open her arms and Michael embraced her in a tight hug. It lasted several seconds. "Goodnight pumpkin," she said, "See you in the morning." It was weird. Was it some kind of ritual they had? Like saying grace or picnics? I should have been warned... Michael's mother smiled at me and held her arms out. I froze like a deer caught in headlights. Was I supposed to hug Michael's mum? Who goes around hugging other people's chil... She grabbed me and held me tight, rocking side to side. Her fluffy pink robe was warm and smelled like apple laundry detergent. "Goodnight, David," she said, "See you in the morning."

I rode my bike home the next day, before lunch as agreed. My mother was on the couch in our living room watching daytime television. I approached her with my arms out like an idiot. It was something new but I'd decided to go for it. She asked what I was doing and I explained I was giving her a hug.

"Why? Were you molested?"
"No."
"What's wrong then?"
"Nothing."
"Well I'm sure it can wait until the commercial break then. *Coronation Street* is on and Billy just confronted Deidre about her affair with Baldwin."

You couldn't pause television in those days. There was no such thing as 'on demand' or even any way to record programs. If you missed something, too bad, wait for the re-run in four or five years. It made the punishment of not being allowed to watch television after dinner if you'd done something wrong an actual punishment. You'd hear about all the exciting things that happened in that night's episode of *Quantum Leap* from kids at school the next day and wish your parents were dead. If I were to tell my offspring that he wasn't allowed to watch a program on television, he'd just say, "Fine, I'll watch it online later." Likewise with being sent to your room. When I was sent to my room as a kid, there was nothing to do so I'd just lie on my bed being angry and wait. My offspring has cable television, gaming consoles, a smartphone, and a computer in his room. The only way to punish him is to turn off the Wi-Fi hub. Once, when he was being particularly annoying, I took the hub with me on an overnight work trip. He sent me furious messages for a couple of hours but eventually ran out of data on his phone.

My mother held me awkwardly, lightly, like one might politely embrace a distant relative at a function. There was no rocking side to side or apple scented warm fluffy pink robe. After a few seconds she patted my back and said, "Okay, that's enough, you're blocking the television and I haven't seen this advertisement for paper towels."

It was the first time I ever remember hugging my mother. Or my mother hugging me. The second time we awkwardly hugged was many years later at my grandfather's funeral. I worked out what was wrong though, what was missing, why her mechanical anxious hug wasn't the same as the safe calming hug from Michael's mother. Mother's Day was just a few weeks away and I convinced my father to take me to K-mart.

"Happy mother's day!"
"A pink robe?"
"Yes. You should put it on."
"I don't wear pink. And I don't wear polyester. Did you keep the receipt? I'll exchange it for an ironing board cover."

I realize at this point you're probably rolling your eyes and muttering, "Oh, please, my mother made me work at a gloryhole when I was six and sold me to gypsies when I was ten," but I'm getting to the fucked up bit and this isn't about you.

My father had twelve affairs that I know of. I'm sure there were more. For years it seemed like there was a new one every couple of months. They were always with wives of friends and the affair always came out and my parents would sit with the other couple in our backyard 'talking it out'. My sister and I often listened through the bathroom window, giving each other wide-eyed looks as sexual encounters were described in detail and voices became raised. Once, my father was punched in the nose and he had to go to hospital.

By the seventh or eighth affair we didn't bother listening at the window, we'd heard it all before and knew to be quiet for a few weeks and then things would go back to normal. But one time it didn't. Maybe it was because the affair was with my mother's best friend, Rosemary. Maybe it was because my father didn't just brush it off as 'a mistake that shouldn't have happened' like he usually did, but instead said he had feelings for Rosemary. That he loved her and she felt the same.

I was sitting in the front seat of our station wagon, Leith was in the back. My mother had told us to quickly pack a bag of clothes and get in the car. My father tried to stop her leaving but he didn't try very hard. I think the cricket was on. I don't know where my mother was planning to take us, or if she even knew. Maybe she intended to work that out while she was driving. Ten or fifteen minutes from our house, my mother turned onto an open stretch of road that went all the way to the next town. It was mostly straight and surrounded by farmland and gum trees. Sometimes my friend Michael and I rode our bikes there because a side road led to a pond with turtles in it.

I noticed we were speeding and asked my mother to slow down. She looked at me, looked in the rear-vision mirror at my sister, then pushed the accelerator pedal to the floor. I remember my sister yelling and the engine screaming, and my mother, expressionless, purposely turning the steering wheel to head towards a large gum tree.

We must have been travelling a hundred miles per hour when we left the road. The car slid and dirt and gravel pelted the windows. My mother wrestled with the steering wheel, but she had no control at that point. We missed the target gum tree, glanced off a second, and hit a third. It wasn't a head-on crash; the glance from the second tree had spun the car enough to take a drivers-side impact. It had also slowed us down somewhat and, although the vehicle was a complete write-off, there were no life-threatening injuries. My mother broke her left wrist and Leith suffered superficial cuts to her face from a shattered rear window, but I only received bruises and a realization. Or maybe confirmation of a realization I'd had years before.

Diane stated in the accident report that she was going the speed limit and had attempted to steer around an animal on the road. I think she said it was a chicken. I didn't see any chicken though.

A few months after the accident, my father ran off with the lady who did the member's fees and match scheduling at his tennis club. They eventually married and, fifteen years later, she cheated on him with a security guard named Gary. I didn't see Diane much after my father left. The transparent performance was no longer necessary and there was a lock on her bedroom door. My sister and I survived on tomato soup and I left home when I was fourteen. Leith had her first kid to guy named Jeans Socksandkeys around that time and moved into a caravan in a field.

When I told Holly that Diane had died, she said she was sorry, and that it was okay to cry, and asked if I wanted her stay home from work. I didn't need her to stay home or apologise for the death of a woman I hardly knew. And I didn't cry. The last time I cried was when a squirrel I rescued died. I bawled my eyes out for hours and I still miss him years later. Sure, he was a pretty awesome squirrel, but the fact that a rodent's death had more impact on me than my mother's should be a pretty clear indicator of the fucks I give. Holly gave me a hug anyway, which was nice. Hugs are always nice.

I walked down the hallway to Seb's bedroom a few minutes ago. He was playing *League of Warcraft* on his computer. Seventy-five percent of Seb's days are spent playing *League of Warcraft*, with the remaining twenty-five percent split between sleeping and microwaving Hot Pockets. I gave him a big hug, with side-to-side action, and he asked me what the hug was for.

"Nothing," I told him, "I just love you."
"Gay," he replied, "Shut the door on your way out, I'm streaming to two-hundred people and I'm in ranked and on promotional divisions."

I have no idea what any of that meant but it was a bit rude so I switched off the Wi-Fi.

JAN   2021

31
SUNDAY

I went in to the office this morning; I needed to spiral bind a document and the cheapest Trubind® I could find on Amazon is $139.95

There were cheaper brands available but it took me five years to work out the office binder and I'm not starting from scratch now. Someone really needs to make one that you just stick the paper in and push a button.

"And this is the spiral binder, David. Put these gloves and goggles on and I'll show you how to operate it."

"You don't just stick the paper in and push a button?"

"Hahaha. No. Stand well back while I while I prime the horbinator and insert the noid into the ferve. If you hear a noise like a ball bearing dropped into an empty glass, run. Don't look back, just run."

FEB 2021
1
MONDAY

Mike is in a particularly bad mood today. I agreed to meet him at the agency this morning to help turn 'Jennifer's office' into 'new person's office'. Mike collected Jennifer's belongings for her husband a few weeks after she died, but there were still items that personalised the space. Apparently the new person isn't allowed to have anything that could be described as 'That's Jen's.'

"What about this pen holder?"

"That's Jen's."

"The new HR manager is going to need something to put pens in."

"Then swap Jen's with Melissa's, the new person can have Melissa's pen holder."

"They're identical."

"It shouldn't be a problem then, should it? Just swap the pen holders and shut up about it. I don't really want to be doing this either. Let's just get it done quickly so we can both go home."

"What about this stapler?"

"That's Jen's."

FEB 2021
2
TUESDAY

I received my first dose of the Moderna Covid-19 vaccination this morning. The vaccinations were held at the county fairgrounds, in a building usually reserved for pig racing or something.

"My pig came first at the county fair last week. That's his fourth blue ribbon this year."
"Wow, he must be fast."
"He is."

I've only been to the county fair once. Lynyrd Skynyrd was playing and Holly told me he was a rave DJ. It wasn't a he at all, it was a group of old guys in denim jackets singing about eagles. Half the audience were the kind of people who wear knives on their belts and the other half were bussed in from surrounding retirement facilities. I did get a fried pickle though. And a funnel cake. Also, a guy wearing a cowboy hat tried to pick me up.

"You a faggot?"
"No, sorry. Have you tried Grindr?"

Some people have reportedly felt ill after receiving the vaccine, but apart from a bit of a sore arm, I feel fine. Better than fine really; I feel relieved I guess, but also proud. I didn't really do anything apart from stand in line and get jabbed, but, as I exited the building, an old guy nodded and gave me the thumbs up.

It was a small gesture, one he gave everyone exiting the building, but it was as if he was saying, "Good job, I'm proud of you, thank you for doing your part." It's probably how soldiers feel when people say, "Thank you for your service." Really, I should get a discount on July 4th mattress sales for my sacrifice. I'm not a fan of lines, or of being jabbed. Plus I had to drive there and find a parking spot. You're welcome.

Also, while I was waiting in line to enter the building, a man with a beard drove slowly past in his pickup truck and yelled, "Baaaaaaaaa!" like a sheep. I guess he also felt he was doing his part and was probably quite proud of his witty onomatopoeian simile. An old lady in the line yelled back, "Oh fuck off, Gavin, grow some balls. And tell your mom I want my baking tray back!" so I'm not sure if Gavin's insult was directed at all of us or just his mom's friend. Gavin did a little burnout when he left the parking lot, so that was pretty cool. It's not that hard to do burnouts on gravel though.

Having lived in the United States for over ten years, one might assume I'd be accustomed to the odd behaviour of

Americans. They still manage to surprise me though. Reason and logic are simply hurdles to Americans; some jump over them, some roll under them, and some bypass them altogether by cutting across the field to the finishing line where they declare themselves the winner.

It's a lot like living with three-hundred-million toddlers - half of which are the 'stomp your feet until you get all the Lego' type and the other half are the type that eats dirt. That's a generalization of course; there are toddlers who share their crayons, and gifted toddlers who manage not to shit themselves every ten minutes, but the strengths and civic mindedness are, for the most part, drowned out by the stomping, crunching, and shitting.

Balance just isn't a thing with Americans, everything is black and white and them and us. There's often a bit of confusion about who the 'them and us' are, but nobody will admit it.

"The stock market has never been higher!"
"Oh, you have stocks?"
"No, but if I did they'd be higher."
"Sure. How are the wife and kids?"
"Doing well. Sharon wrangled a third shift at Waffle House and we received our government stimulus check this week so Betty Sue's rickets medicine is covered."

During an outing to Home Depot recently, I saw an old guy wearing a t-shirt that said, *I don't need a mask, I have Jesus.*

The guy was at the checkout buying a large roll of patterned linoleum - possibly reflooring his trailer with his government stimulus check - and, as is common in this rural region of Virginia, he was open-carrying a handgun on his right hip. The only deduction one can make from this is that protection by Jesus is limited to fending off airborne droplets and, for all other threats, you're on your own.

He looked like the kind of guy who would have exceptional health care coverage though, so I'm sure he'll be fine even if Jesus is distracted for a moment - perhaps to give a child cancer - and misses a droplet.

Early in the pandemic, before it was even called a pandemic, I asked my coworker Ben what he'd do if the virus got really bad and he told me he'd go to a deserted island to wait it out. Which sounds nice but I'm not sure how he'd get there or how he'd survive. He has no boating experience, I've seen him freak out over a moth in his office, and he doesn't eat meat or fish. Once, during a client lunch meeting, Ben discovered a bit of bacon in his salad and started gagging so badly he couldn't breathe and had to lie on the floor. What's he going to eat on his island? Bark?

"What are you going to eat on your island, Ben? Bark?"
"No, I'll eat coconuts. They're high in protein and fibre."
"I'm sure they are. Plus you can make monkeys out of the shells when you get bored. For company."
"I won't be bored, I'll be too busy doing island things."

"Like what?"

"Swimming and relaxing."

"Well that sounds nice. Ignoring the fact you don't own a boat and have no navigation experience, I'm surprised you haven't left already."

"If the virus gets bad, I'll just steal a boat."

"You'll steal someone's boat?"

"Yes, from a jetty."

"And just point it out to sea, hit go, and hope you come across an island with coconuts?"

"I have Google Maps."

I asked the same question to a few other coworkers; Walter stated that if civilization collapsed he'd go camping and live off squirrels, Jennifer said it was an unrealistic scenario because it's just like a bad case of the flu, and Gary said, "If it means never having to listen to idiotic conversations about coconut islands again, I hope I catch Covid and die."

When I was in grade eight or nine, our class watched a movie called *The Day After*, about a nuclear attack and the aftermath that follows. There's a scene where a family is in a bunker or basement rationing food, and, after watching the movie, our teacher had us write an assignment about who we'd let in to our bunker if space and food was limited, and why. Most of the class wrote that they would include their parents, siblings, friends and pets - maybe their grandparents and relatives. I chose Jeannie from *I Dream of Jeannie* and I still stand by my choice.

These days, if I had to choose who to let into a bunker, excluding television genies, I'd probably only include my partner Holly and offspring Seb. Even those two are iffy. Seb eats and shits his own weight every few hours, and Holly would want to bring the dogs, Trivial Pursuit, and her karaoke machine into the bunker. I'd rather stay outside and take my chances to be honest.

"Who's up for karaoke?"

"Actually, I was just about to head out. Might scavenge for food amongst the ruins while fending off giant mutant radioactive cockroaches for a bit."

"How long will you be?"

"That depends on whether I'm captured by post-apocalyptic warlords or not."

"Okay. Bring back some toilet paper. We're almost out."

FEB   2021
3
WEDNESDAY

The HR manager and graphic designer positions were only posted Monday and we've already received several resumés for both. The salaries offered are industry standard so at least something positive came from 'the Josh thing'. I'm calling it 'the Josh thing' even though Mike refers to it as 'David's massive fuckup with tight pants guy'. Again, some accountability could be attributed to the salary offered, but accountability isn't something people like to share. It's like reverse fries. Maybe old cold ones. Or maybe more like helping put sheets on the bed.

Thankfully, Mike is more upset about 'Ben's nuzzle fuckup' at the moment; the client rejected the boxes with the stickers. This means we will have to cover the reprinting costs after all and I watched movies about magic for nothing. Also, if Ben hadn't made the mistake in the first place, I wouldn't have met Josh, which means full accountability for the Josh thing should be attributed to Ben. Really, people need to own up to their mistakes and learn from them. It's not even the first time Ben has had an error make it to print; there's 8000 Herbal Essence bottles on shelves somewhere with the words 'rinse and repeal' on the back.

From: Mike Campbell
Date: Thursday 4 February 2021 9.38am
To: All Staff
Subject: Glo_2O

Morning,

Has everyone had a chance to try the Glo_2O flavor drops?

We're are all back in the office next week so I've scheduled Wednesday morning for a group meeting to discuss the tagline. If anyone has any thoughts in the meantime, forward them to me.

Mike

....

From: Walter Bowers
Date: Thursday 4 February 2021 9.57am
To: All Staff
Subject: Re: Glo_2O

They turned my pee blue

From: David Thorne
Date: Thursday 4 February 2021 10.07am
To: All Staff
Subject: Re: Re: Glo_2O

Mike,

As Walter has come up with the perfect tagline, do we still need to have a meeting on Wednesday?

David

....

From: Mike Campbell
Date: Thursday 4 February 2021 10.12am
To: Walter Bowers **Cc:** All Staff
Subject: Re: Re: Re: Glo_2O

Walter, how much did you use?

Mike

....

From: Walter Bowers
Date: Thursday 4 February 2021 10.21am
To: Mike Campbell
Subject: Re: Re: Re: Re: Glo_2O

just some squirts like maybe half.

From: Mike Campbell
Date: Thursday 4 February 2021 10.26am
To: Walter Bowers **Cc:** All Staff
Subject: Re: Re: Re: Re: Re: Glo$_2$O

You're meant to use a few drops. They're called flavor drops, not flavor squirts. Half what? Half the bottle?

Mike

....

From: Walter Bowers
Date: Thursday 4 February 2021 10.34am
To: Mike Campbell
Subject: Re: Re: Re: Re: Re: Re: Glo$_2$O

Nobody told me that. i thought it was strong it tasted like metal and made my teeth hut.

FEB 2021
5
FRIDAY

Three days. That's how long I have left before we're all expected to stop working remotely and return to the agency. There are so many things I meant to do and didn't get around to because I thought I had another two or three months. Like learning the piano or inventing something and taking it on *Shark Tank*.

"So it's a baseball cap with a small oval hole cut in the brim."
"That's right. It's a cap toothbrush holder."
'What if people need more than one toothbrush while they're out?"
"It comes in one, two, and three hole models."
"What are your sales?"

I also wanted to buy cryptocurrency. My friend Ross made four grand on Dogecoin and bought a jetski. Thanks for ruining that dream, Mike. You may have cost me millions.

Update:

Right, I worked out how to buy cryptocurrency. It wasn't that hard. I've lost eight hundred dollars on Robinhood in three hours.

Okay, I'm an expert on cryptocurrency now. I'm four thousand dollars down but that's because I've been 'buying the dips'. That's a crypto term, sorry for going all technical. I'm actually thinking about quitting my job at the agency and becoming a day trader. That way I can work from wherever I want; my yacht, my plane, my jetski.

Basically, trading cryptocurrency consists of 80% watching wiggly lines, 15% FOMO, and 5% battery left. Here's a handy guide to what the wiggly lines mean.

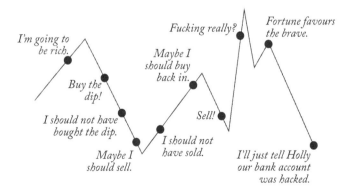

FEB **2021**

7

SUNDAY

I saw on the local news tonight that the village idiot who waves and smiles at cars while leaning against a giant cross made out of deck planks, was hit by a car today.

Apparently an elderly woman lost control of her vehicle at the intersection and hit another vehicle, which veered onto the median strip. I wonder if the religious nutter was smiling and waving as he went through the windscreen? He wasn't killed - if he were this page might be considered bad taste - but he's in the hospital with a broken collar bone so that should keep him off the median strip for a while.

Also, I learned his name. It's Chuck Pears the 3rd. I bet he got teased a lot at school. Chuck isn't a name in Australia. Because it's stupid. So is giving your child a name they have to use a number with to identify which one they are.

"Did you hear Chuck Pears got hit by a car today?"
"Which one?"
"The third one."
"Good."

FEB **2021**

8

MONDAY

Everyone is back at the agency today and, as Melissa was concerned about her dog Petie experiencing separation anxiety, some bright spark had the idea to make the first day back 'bring your foul creatures to work day'.

There's been six dogfights, Ben was bitten, and Jodie's cat had some kind of seizure. It's in the stationery room listening to Vivaldi with the lights off so bad luck if anyone needs a pen.

Also, someone's dog took a dump on the stairs and Gary slipped on it. He's currently pretending his leg is broken and looking up state compensation laws online while trying to convince Ben to join him in a class action.

Zero work has been done today - everyone's too busy cleaning shit off everything and complaining about the smell - but at least we're all back in the office because "Working remotely simply isn't as productive."

FEB 2021
9
TUESDAY

Ben called in sick this morning. He thinks he has lockjaw and is demanding Melissa email a scan of Petie's rabies vaccination records to him.

Mike wore a black suit to work today and the office is covered in pet hair; you can see it floating in the air when the sun hits it right. He's currently standing in his office with his arms out, spinning slowly like a rotisserie chicken, while Melissa vacuums him with a DustBuster.

From: Mike Campbell
Date: Tuesday 9 February 2021 9.42am
To: Melissa Peters **Cc:** All Staff
Subject: Pet hair

Melissa,

We won't be having any more pet days. If you're concerned about Petey being alone, buy another dog.

I brushed my hand across my desk a minute ago and it looked like I was wearing a wool glove. Please call the cleaners and tell them we need them to come in immediately. I don't care if we have to pay emergency rates. The amount of hair behind the photocopier has to be a fire hazard.

I have another meeting at 10.30 so I'll need you to vacuum me again.

Mike

....

From: Melissa Peters
Date: Tuesday 9 February 2021 9.57am
To: Mike Campbell
Subject: Re: Pet hair

Its Petie not Petey.

Mel

....

From: Mike Campbell
Date: Tuesday 9 February 2021 10.02am
To: Melissa Peters
Subject: Re: Re: Pet hair

Melissa,

I don't give a fuck.

Mike

Our dog Bansky was a participant in yesterday's shedfest and I'm fairly certain most of the hair is his. He sheds enough to stuff a cushion every five minutes and, when he has the zoomies, leaves contrails. I wasn't keen on taking him to work, as I hate him, but sometimes you have to participate in group activities even if you dislike the group and activity. Like family dinners.

I don't really hate Banksy, it's more of a general disdain. He's some kind of dalmatian / labrador / goat mix and only has four states of being: farting, sleeping, zooming, and staring at the fridge. If I'm out anywhere with him and someone asks what breed he is, I tell them that I don't know because he's not my dog, I'm just looking after him for a week while his owner is vacationing in Arizona, and that my dog at home is much better looking and smarter.

"Oh, what breed is your dog at home?"
"Like Lassie. But with short hair."
"And he can really speak three languages and play chess?"
"Yes. And he's a geologist."

I didn't actually see much of Banksy yesterday. He spent the morning begging in the kitchen (apparently he ate a ham sandwich, half a block of cheese, six sushi rolls, a bowl of risotto, and a Big Mac) and spent the afternoon in a food coma behind the photocopier. I had to carry him to my car at the end of the day and drive home with the windows down as his farts smelled like fish and cheese.

Also, at some point yesterday, Jodie's cat vomited in the stationery room. Mike made Jodie carry the spiral binder outside and throw it in the dumpster.

From: Melissa Peters
Date: Tuesday 9 February 2021 11.04am
To: All Staff
Subject: Spiral binder

Hi,

Just so you know Mike threw out the spiral binder so nobody can spiral bind anything today. They dont sell that one anymore so I ordered a different one. A yellow one. Guess we will all have to learn how to use the new one now because Mike had to make a point instead of just washing it off.

He threw the rug in the kitchen out as well just because it had a tiny stain on it.

Mel

....

From: Mike Campbell
Date: Tuesday 9 February 2021 11.09am
To: Melissa Peters
Subject: Re: Spiral binder

Fuck off Melissa. Take some responsibility for your actions.

Mike

FEB 2021

10

WEDNESDAY

We had a group meeting this morning to discuss the tagline for a new beverage 'enhancement' product. It's one of those little bottles of concentrated chemicals that you add to water to make it taste like aluminium mixed with blueberry, watermelon, or kiwi fruit. I've tried a couple of the competitor's brands and they all taste the same.

Mike had arranged the bottles on the boardroom table with several bottles of water. We were meant to add a few drops, try it, then express how much we loved it. Nobody loved it though. The stuff was dreadful.

"Okay," said Mike, "it's not going to kill you so let's just get on with the process. First thoughts Rebecca?"

"I'm sorry, I can't drink it, it's just too chemically."

"Okay, well I'm not going to write that on the whiteboard, we're looking for positive attributes. Walter?"

"Just good things about it?"

"Yes."

"It's better than just water I suppose. Not much though. I'd rather have a Coke."

"Okay, I'll add 'better than water' on the whiteboard but I was really hoping for more something a bit more enthusiastic."

"And it makes the water look like a glow stick," Walter added, "like you have at raves."

Mike nodded, "I won't write that down but thank you, Walter. Ben?"

"It kind of tastes like those scented Sharpies you used to have as kids."

"You ate the Sharpies?"

"No, it tastes like they smelled. Not as nice though."

"Right. David?"

"Walter's correct, they do look like glow sticks. You should write that down. Leave Ben's Sharpie comment off though, that was just stupid."

"You're stupid."

"David, there's no stupid suggestions during brainstorming sessions," Mike stated, "If people are worried about their suggestion being called stupid, nobody will suggest anything."

"You're correct and I apologise, you should add 'tastes like Sharpies' to the whiteboard."

"No, I'm not going to add that. Jodie?"

"If you take a small sip it's drinkable. It's only when you take a big drink that you get the bad metal taste. It's the artificial sweetener. It's sweet, but it's too sweet, but not nice sweet."

"Right, so the positive aspect is?"

"It's okay if you only drink a tiny bit. And maybe have some plain water afterwards to wash away the taste."

"So nothing positive then. Gary?"

"I'm not the best person to ask. I don't drink water."

"Everyone drinks water, Gary. You'd die if you didn't."

"I drink coffee."

"There's water in coffee, Gary."

"Yes, but I'm not going to add kiwi fruit flavor drops to it, am I? What a stupid fucking statement."

"Okay, well I personally didn't mind the watermelon flavor and thought it was quite refreshing so I'm adding 'refreshing' to the whiteboard. Any other thoughts? No? So we have 'it's better than water', 'looks like a glow stick', and is 'refreshing'. This has been a total waste of time. Yes David?"

"Perhaps we're just going about this the wrong way. We have to come up with a happy tagline regardless of how sad this tastes, so let's drink something pleasant instead and run the suggestions off that."

"A different product?"

"Yes, a delicious one. We're not going to come up with a 'taste the rainbow' tagline drinking this."

"Okay, that actually makes sense. Melissa, go to the closest gas station and grab every flavor of Snapple they have."

"Snapple?"

"Yes, it's delicious. Yes, Walter?"

"Can I get a Coke? I don't like Snapple."

"No, you're drinking Snapple."

From: David Thorne
Date: Wednesday 10 February 2021 2.52pm
To: Mike Campbell, Ben Townsend
Subject: Glo₂O

Okay,

Initial concept for tagline application following this morning's meeting. It's either this or Gary's idea for a musical. Ben and I will go over tweaks this afternoon but we have a few weeks to storyboard it properly before the client presentation.

Commercial:

Large audience of 20-somethings at a DJ rave. They're dancing and holding up water bottles. Electronic dance music reaches the peak anticipation moment... then drops. All the bottles light up with different colours like glow sticks. Glo₂O logo. Tagline: *When the flavor drops.*

Print media:

Image of large audience at a DJ rave holding up coloured glowing bottles. Logo and tagline.

If we can tie in a well known DJ all the better. Also, Walter has requested that he be in the audience because, "The glow sticks were my idea and I'm a really good dancer."

David

From: Ashley Hilditch
Date: Thursday 11 February 2021 2.55pm
To: David Thorne
Subject: Pondvac Artwork

Hello,

I'm doing freelance work for Howie Dunbrik and he asked me to contact you regarding the existing Pondvac artwork. If I could get the photos and files from you that would be much appreciated.

Thank you, Ashley

....

From: David Thorne
Date: Thursday 11 February 2021 3.24pm
To: Ashley Hilditch
Subject: Re: Pondvac Artwork

Hello Ashley,

Howie is fully aware that he has an outstanding invoice with our agency going back to August 2019. This is probably why he asked you to source the photos and artwork from us.

Please let Howie know that once we have received the outstanding payment of $14,822.00, we will be happy to hand over all project artwork and commissioned photos.

On a personal note, best of luck with this client. He was abusive towards our creative director after learning he's gay, referred to our office manager as 'dumb but fuckable', and commissioned us to undertake work while knowingly trading insolvent. I'd recommend requesting payment prior to delivery of any work you do for him.

Regards, David

....

From: Ashley Hilditch
Date: Thursday 11 February 2021 3.38pm
To: David Thorne
Subject: Re: Re: Pondvac Artwork

Yeah, I kind of got that vibe from him. He was wearing a MAGA cap at our first meeting and kept calling me sweetie. Unfortunately, as a freelancer, I have to take what clients I can get at the moment.

Thank you for getting back to me so quickly and I appreciate your honesty. BTW, I had a look at your agency's website and you guys have done some really nice work.

Ashley

From: David Thorne
Date: Thursday 11 February 2021 3.52pm
To: Ashley Hilditch
Subject: Re: Re: Re: Pondvac Artwork

Ashley,

I've worked freelance so I understand completely. And I appreciate the feedback; we have a couple of good designers. I had a quick look at your website and you also have some nice work. Your product packaging is very clean.

We're actually hiring for a graphic designer at the moment and I'd be happy to send you a link to the job description if you think that's something you'd consider. We do a lot of packaging and we screen clients to avoid future Howies.

Regards, David

....

From: Ashley Hilditch
Date: Thursday 11 February 2021 3.57pm
To: David Thorne
Subject: Re: Re: Re: Re: Pondvac Artwork

That's definitely something I'd consider.

Thank you, Ashley

From: Howie Dunbrik
Date: Friday 12 February 2021 9.50am
To: David Thorne
Subject: Files

Hey asshole

What kind of petty piece of shit would tell someone that works for me that I owe you money? Is that what you think is professional you fucking loser?

The work your agency did for PCS two years ago wasn't used. That company doesn't exist anymore. This is a completely new company.

Refusing to give me files that are no use to you at all isn't professional in any way, it's just you choosing to be a prick about it.

I'd reconsider sending Ashley those files if I were you. I'm not someone you want to have as an enemy. You have until the end of the day.

Howie Dunbrik

From: David Thorne
Date: Friday 12 February 2021 10.07am
To: Howie Dunbrik
Subject: Verification required

Thank you for contacting us.

As part of our agency's internal email filter system, we require verification that you are not a robot before your email can be delivered.

Please select and reply with one of the following to proceed:

I am not a robot: [**Y**] or [**N**]

Also, don't forget to subscribe to *Blue Blanket* - our socialist lifestyle and liberal agenda newsletter. This month's edition includes a handy map to Confederate statue locations and expert reviews of angle grinders.

....

From: Howie Dunbrik
Date: Friday 12 February 2021 10.12am
To: David Thorne
Subject: Re: Verification required

Y

From: David Thorne
Date: Friday 12 February 2021 10.25am
To: Howie Dunbrik
Subject: Subscription confirmation

Thank you for subscribing to *Blue Blanket*.

You should receive your first edition shortly. Be sure to check out our 6-page list of gender-neutral pronouns, tips on front yard BLM sign placement, and an illustrated guide to tuck techniques.

To confirm your subscription, please select and reply with one of the following:

[**Y**] or [**N**]

....

From: Howie Dunbrik
Date: Friday 12 February 2021 10.29pm
To: David Thorne
Subject: Re: Subscription confirmation

N

From: David Thorne
Date: Friday 12 February 2021 10.37am
To: Howie Dunbrik
Subject: Verification required

You have answered: N: I am not a robot.

Your email has not been delivered for the following reason: You are not not a robot.

Secondary verification is required before we can deliver your email. To proceed, please select and reply with the number of sheep in the following image:

[**2**] [**7**] [**128**]

....

From: Howie Dunbrik
Date: Friday 12 February 2021 10.41am
To: David Thorne
Subject: Re: Verification required

128

From: David Thorne
Date: Friday 12 February 2021 10.55am
To: Howie Dunbrik
Subject: Verification required

You have answered: 128

Your email has not been delivered for the following reason: Incorrect number. There are 129 sheep in the image.

Additional verification is required before we can deliver your email. To proceed, please select and reply with the number of massive dildos in the following image:

[3]   [**128**]

....

From: Howie Dunbrik
Date: Friday 12 February 2021 11.02am
To: David Thorne
Subject: Re: Verification required

Watch your back loser. I know where you work.

From: David Thorne
Date: Friday 12 February 2021 11.17am
To: Howie Dunbrik
Subject: Verification required

You have answered: I'm a sad little man, pay attention to me as I jump up and down and make flaccid threats. I also have a duck's name, use implicit anti-gay bias to shield my same-sex desires, and thought the sheep photo was part of an actual verification process.

Your email has not been delivered for the following reason: Incorrect selection. The correct answer is 3.

Additional verification is required before we can deliver your email. To proceed, please reply with the characters from the following captcha:

i should pay my bills

....

From: Howie Dunbrik
Date: Friday 12 February 2021 11.24am
To: David Thorne
Subject: Re: Verification required

When you least expect it.

From: David Thorne
Date: Friday 12 February 2021 11.36am
To: Howie Dunbrik
Subject: Re: Re: Verification required

Howard,

I'd probably least expect it while vacationing in another state or country. Perhaps while swimming.

Or maybe on my death bed. I'd be old and frail and as I whisper to my wife, "Holly, there's something I need to tell you, I was the one who..." you'd burst in, probably wearing your $20 gas station biker shades, waddle towards the equipment keeping me alive, and attempt to pull a plug. There's no way I'd be expecting that.

As your threats are in writing - effectively cementing them as the flaccid wailings of a dimwitted bully with no other recourse - I have two options at this point; I've located your files on our server and can either A. Put them in the trash and hit delete, or B. Compress them into a .zip file and send it to you.

If I choose to send you the .zip file, will this bring the matter to a close?

Regards, David

From: Howie Dunbrik
Date: Friday 12 February 2021 11.40am
To: David Thorne
Subject: Re: Re: Re: Verification required

Yes.

....

From: David Thorne
Date: Friday 12 February 2021 11.44am
To: Howie Dunbrik
Subject: Subscription confirmation

Thank you for confirming your subscription to *Blue Blanket*.

FEB 2021
13
SATURDAY

It's almost 10am and Seb and Holly aren't up yet. Maybe they've forgotten it's my birthday. That would actually be preferable.

For some, birthdays are a time to reflect on their accomplishments over the past year and smile and nod. They're probably the type of people who own a whole bitcoin and a Tesla. Maybe an Airbnb. For others, birthdays are an unwelcome reminder that another year has passed without a single memorable accomplishment. A year closer to being discovered dead on the toilet.

I'm somewhere in the middle; I don't own a Tesla or a whole bitcoin, but I have stayed in an Airbnb. I've also had a couple of accomplishments over the past twelve months; I didn't die and I'm not homeless.

I'm fairly apathetic about my birthday - which is probably why Seb and Holly are apathetic about the gifts they get me. I once received a cap with a built-in flashlight and a pair of really thin socks - I think they were the free ones women use to try on shoes in department stores. Last year, Holly gave me a gift card. I can't even remember what store it was for. It might have been JC Penney. I think Seb got me fish food because we were almost out.

It's as if they have an ongoing secret contest to see who can get me the lamest present. There's probably rules, like it can't just be a piece of paper with the letter H on it, but anything between that and a backscratcher shaped like a skeleton's hand goes.

"It's David's birthday next week."
"Game on."
"The fish food is going to be hard to top."
"Yes, but I have a couple of ideas up my sleeve. Which is worse, a USB powered coffee mug or a book about hats?"
"They're both about equal."
"What are you getting him?"
"A packet of drinking straws."
"The bendy type?"
"Pfft. No."
"Nice."

Update:

Seb and Holly didn't forget my birthday. If anything, they went all out this year. Seb got me a 4K documentary about whales, and Holly splurged and got me *two* presents: a bottle of Lithuanian olive oil and a new shower curtain.

FEB 2021
14
SUNDAY

A meteor struck the ground ten miles from the village where we live this morning. I didn't personally see or hear the meteor, but our local news reported there was a bright flash followed by a boom. A reporter covered the event live, two hours after it had happened, from a field. It wasn't the field where the meteor struck - nobody knows where it actually hit - but, according to the reporter, "It probably landed in a field very similar to this one."

It was also covered on the news tonight. Our local weather lady, Aubrey, stated, "Did anyone see or hear the fireball this morning? That's right, there was a fireball in the sky!"

Who calls a meteor a fireball? Aubrey can't possibly have been taught that in meteorology school. Perhaps she went to fireballology school instead.

Also, it's Valentine's Day today. I gave Holly an Athleta gift card and she gave me a 2021 calendar from her bank and a spray-bottle of lens cleaner.

FEB 2021

15

MONDAY

We held the first round of interviews for Jennifer's replacement last week and, despite many of the candidates being highly qualified, Mike found fault with each and every one. Some of his criticisms have been valid - one candidate ate a bag of chips during the interview - but most have been a bit of a stretch. Here's just twelve of Mike's post-interview statements on why the applicant wouldn't be a 'good fit' for the agency:

"She breeds koi. You know what fish people are like."

"Her jacket was pilling, you didn't notice? If she can't be bothered using a lint remover, I can't be bothered giving her a second interview."

"Her tongue was very pointy."

"She was just a bit overenthusiastic. We have enough overenthusiastic people here."

"Who drinks that much water during an interview? Did she come from a desert? You can strike lizard lady off the list."

"She looked a bit windswept."

"You didn't think her pants were too baggy? They were like those pants some people wear for yoga. We don't want yoga people here, they think they're better than everyone else just because they have good balance."

"She didn't say a word about my tie."

"I don't have a problem with a HR manager being male, I have a problem with people who nod that much. This isn't a pantomime."

"There's no way I could look at that thin hair every day."

"Her voice was very deep."

"I just felt like punching her every time she said the word 'flexibility'."

At some point, Mike is going to have to accept that it's impossible to replace Jennifer with Jennifer 2.0 and move on. I told him this and he stated, "I'm not looking for another Jennifer, I just want someone who's as easy to get along with as I am."

Also, Jodie, Walter and I have the first round of interviews for the graphic design position this afternoon. I asked Mike if he's planning to join us in the boardroom, and he replied, "No, I trust Jodie and Walter to make a good decision."

Walter is taking his interviewer role extremely seriously and even wore a tie to work today. It's his Christmas tie, featuring a penguin ice skating, but it still counts. He also went into full professional mode during the interviews and nodded thoughtfully while making statements such as, "Ah, I see your point of view," and, "Can you expand on that?" There were very little instances where these statements were in context, but again, it still counts.

"And then I spent a month as an intern at Ogilvy & Mather after finishing school. Mainly just making coffee and doing errands, but I did learn a lot just from being there."
"Can you expand on that?"
"Um, not really."
Ah, I see your point of view. And do you ride a bicycle?"
"No."
"I do. It's a Cannondale."

From: Walter Bowers
Date: Tuesday 16 February 2021 9.16am
To: David Thorne, Jodie Smythe
Subject: interviews

I know we other designers to interview but we should just tell them the position is taken I think we should hire Ashley because her portfolio was really good.

....

From: David Thorne
Date: Tuesday 16 February 2021 9.21am
To: Walter Bowers
Subject: Re: interviews

Walter,

Of course you do. At one point I thought you were going to tell Ashley you love her. I'm pretty sure I saw you mouth the words.

David

From: Walter Bowers
Date: Tuesday 16 February 2021 9.30am
To: David Thorne
Subject: Re: Re: interviews

No i didnt. I just think shes a good designer and much better than the other ones. The first one was terrible and Jodie just likes the fat one because shes fat as well and that way she wont be the fattest one in the office. her portfolio wasnt even good it had bad typography we shouldent hire her. di you see the way she kerned the word exhibition on the exhibition poster layout it looked like E x hibiti o n.

....

From: David Thorne
Date: Tuesday 16 February 2021 9.24am
To: Walter Bowers
Subject: Re: Re: Re: interviews

Walter,

Slight exaggeration but a valid observation. I wish you'd shown this much concern for typographic skills when I offered Josh the position.

How's he doing by the way?

David

From: Walter Bowers
Date: Tuesday 16 February 2021 9.16am
To: David Thorne
Subject: Re: Re: Re: Re: interviews

Good hes the director of graphics for his own design company called OMJ like oh my gosh but with josh instead of gosh. he said wants me to work for him but i said no because i like getting paid.

....

From: David Thorne
Date: Tuesday 16 February 2021 9.24am
To: Walter Bowers
Subject: Re: Re: Re: Re: Re: interviews

Walter,

Probably wise. There's no such thing as Director of Graphics and the name is stupid.

We have three designers to interview this afternoon. While I agree Ashley's portfolio is excellent, it wouldn't be fair to the others to just cancel their interviews.

Besides, you didn't find Ashley a little flirty? I'm fairly certain I saw her smile and wink at Ben on her way out.

David

From: Walter Bowers
Date: Tuesday 16 February 2021 9.16am
To: David Thorne
Subject: Re: Re: Re: Re: Re: Re: interviews

Shes not flity shes just friendly and as if ben. who wears a hat like that and hes really short and he has a hairy neck have you seen that? all the hair on the back of his neck it goes all the way down. he should shave it.

....

From: David Thorne
Date: Tuesday 16 February 2021 9.24am
To: Walter Bowers
Subject: Re: Re: Re: Re: Re: Re: Re: interviews

Walter,

Some girls have a thing for hats and hairy necks. I think I saw her eyes sparkle as well.

David

....

From: Walter Bowers
Date: Tuesday 16 February 2021 9.24am
To: David Thorne
Subject: Re: Re: Re: Re: Re: Re: Re: Re: interviews

they didnt sparkle for him theyr just spakly.

FEB 2021
17
WEDNESDAY

Melissa devotes a good portion of each day to making her signature 'I'm livid and I want everyone to be aware of it' face. Once, after being told to remove a 'paint by numbers' painting of two Victorian women holding umbrellas from the boardroom wall, she made the face for an entire week.

The face, which looks more like Melissa is pushing out a particularly difficult poo than seething, is generally accompanied by harmless drawer slamming, loud keyboard clacking, and going to Starbucks without asking if anyone else wants something.

This morning, however, after being told she couldn't grow a herb garden on her desk, Melissa threw a can of soup at a bus. She claims she wasn't aiming for the bus, she was aiming for a tree, but this doesn't really explain anything.

Update 11.10am

Super excitement in the office. Melissa is currently speaking to a police officer in the front foyer and everyone has stopped work to listen. Ben has his mouth wide open because he read somewhere that if you open your jaw, it moves the bones in your ear allowing you to hear better. I missed half the conversation because of Ben's jaw story, but from what I can tell, the police officer is just as puzzled as I am as to why anyone would throw a can of soup at a tree. Jodie is loving this. If her glee was tangible it would be like a huge sun.

Update 11.15am

Mike once watched an episode of *LA Law* so he's decided to get involved. He asked the officer if there is a specific law against throwing cans of soup at trees and was informed there's no specific law, as such, but trees on the sidewalk are government property and intentionally damaging one could be classed as vandalism.

Update 11.45am

Melissa has to go to court next month. She's panicking a bit because she has a criminal record for shoplifting an eyeliner pen from Sephora in 2012. She's also convinced that the officer would have let her off with a warning if Mike hadn't butted in. The face is currently at level ten.

Also, Gary missed all the excitement and, when he returned from a meeting, he asked, "Why is there a can of soup on the front counter?" Melissa replied, "That's none of your fucking business, Gary," and Gary stated, "Well, there's a dent in it, you shouldn't eat it, you can get botulism from dented cans."

FEB 2021

18
THURSDAY

After much deliberation, Jodie and I decided to offer Ashley the graphic design position. Normally we'd hold second interviews, but they're honestly just a waste of everyone's time. What are you going to learn in a second interview that you didn't in the first? What the person's second outfit choice is? What if they don't have a second outfit planned? They can't wear the same outfit they wore to the first interview. It means an emergency trip to TJ Maxx.

It's easier for guys than girls of course, we can wear the same suit and even the same shirt and socks every day if we want. It's good to mix it up with a different tie occasionally but even that's not obligatory. I have a favourite suit and tie and only wear white shirts, so every photo of me taken over the last ten years looks like I'm at the same event.

"They must have had a good buffet at that event, David."
"What are you getting at?"

Walter doesn't know about the decision yet, so I'm going to tell him we chose Gwen, the bad typography girl.

From: David Thorne
Date: Thursday 18 February 2021 1.44pm
To: Walter Bowers
Subject: Applicants

Walter,

Thank you for your help with the interviewing process.

Jodie and I went over the resumés this morning and have decided Gwen will be the 'best fit' for the agency.

Jodie offered her the position this morning and she has accepted.

She starts next week and will be working closely with you for the first few months. Please clear half your desk for her to share.

David

....

From: Walter Bowers
Date: Thursday 18 February 2021 1.52pm
To: David Thorne
Subject: Re: Applicants

Is gwen the fat one? this is bullshit i hate this place.

Update 2.45pm

Walter is rebelling the decision to hire Gwen and has demanded it be put to a vote. He spent ten minutes in my office recreating Gwen's kerning of the word exhibition on my white board and provided an exhaustive list of why Ashley would be the better choice - including, "The name Gwen is just horrible to say, go on say it, horrible isn't it?" and, "She wears her hair in a bun. Rebecca already wears her hair in a bun. That means there'll be two."

I'm with him on the bun thing. Rebecca looks like she's balancing a coconut on her head.

"I just don't get it."
"No, neither do I. It has to take more effort than just putting it in a ponytail, and ponytails look great."
"No, I mean why Gwen? Her portfolio was shit. How could anyone think her portfolio was better than Ashley's? We should have a vote."
"Jodie and I already took a vote. Jodie won by putting two hands up. I didn't know you could do that."
"You can't!"

Update 3.05pm

Jodie just came back from a meeting and asked Walter if he was pleased with the decision. Walter replied, "No, why would I be? There should have been a vote. A fair one where we put votes in a hat."

FEB 2021
19
FRIDAY

Melissa learned recently that her name comes from the Greek word for 'bee'.

Apparently this explains why her favorite colour is yellow and why she's never been stung by a bee. Firstly, who's never been stung by a bee? Has she never been outside? Secondly, bees don't have a list of people's names. They're not saying to each other, "Yes, I realize she stepped on you, but she gets a pass because she's on the Melissa list."

As Melissa is now an official bee, she ordered herself a bright yellow office chair from Amazon. It was delivered an hour ago. All our other chairs are by Herman Miller (Embody in blue, our brand colour) and Mike is currently having a meltdown.

He's sent four emails this morning to all staff about Melissa's 'banana on wheels' being an affront to brand integrity, and there was a heated exchange after Melissa returned from making a coffee to discover Mike had written "NO!" on the backrest of the chair in thick black Sharpie.

I should also note that in keeping with her new bee theme, Melissa wore a yellow dress to work today. The dress is almost the exact colour of the chair and when Melissa is sitting, it looks like two giant peeps spooning. Apparently voicing this observation wasn't helpful.

Unfortunately, due either to Melissa becoming sweaty during the shouting match or the Sharpie not being dry, Melissa now has a large !ON on the back of her dress and is demanding Mike pay restitution.

I considered working from home today because my hair wouldn't go right. I'm glad I didn't.

From: Mike Campbell
Date: Friday 19 February 2021 10.04am
To: Melissa Peters **Cc:** All Staff
Subject: Brand integrity

Melissa,

All future furniture additions for this agency are to approved by me prior to purchase.

This isn't your house. We have standards here.

The front foyer is a client's first impression of the agency. It's not yours to decorate how you wish. I don't give a fuck how many episodes of shabby chic or flea market flip you've watched, you're not an interior designer.

Our Herman Miller chairs cost $1500 each. If your banana on wheels isn't removed within the next 30 minutes, I will wheel it outside and set fire to it.

Mike

....

From: Melissa Peters
Date: Friday 19 February 2021 10.11am
To: Mike Campbell
Subject: Re: Brand integrity

You said I could get a new chair because the plastic bit on the front of mine came off and was rubbing on my leg.

You didnt say it has to be blue.

Mel

From: Mike Campbell
Date: Friday 19 February 2021 10.23am
To: Melissa Peters
Subject: Re: Re: Brand integrity

Melissa,

I didn't say you could purchase a new chair. I said you could SWAP your chair. With one of the others. Gary has a spare one in his office.

I want the yellow chair out of the building before anyone sees it. It looks like a chair old ladies use to sew. This is a branding agency, not Hobby Lobby.

And why is there a flapping bee on your email? I hope you haven't emailed any clients with that on there. It's unprofessional and annoying. Remove it.

Mike

....

From: Melissa Peters
Date: Friday 19 February 2021 10.30am
To: Mike Campbell
Subject: Re: Re: Re: Brand integrity

It doesn't flap when Im writing an email just after its been sent so I dont know how to stop it. Its an animation gif so I don't even know if i can.

This chair is a lot more comfortable than the other one and

I think if I should have to sit in a chair all day I should be comfortable.

Mel

....

From: Mike Campbell
Date: Friday 19 February 2021 10.37am
To: Melissa Peters, David Thorne, Ben Townsend
Subject: Re: Re: Re: Re: Brand integrity

Melissa,

The flapping hasn't got anything to do with it. Why is there a bee on your email at all? Remove it.

And bullshit that cheap piece of shit is more comfortable than a Herman Miller chair. If you find it uncomfortable it's because you sit wrong. You don't get to dilute our brand just because you slouch.

David and Ben, can you believe Melissa is even attempting to justify this?

Mike

From: David Thorne
Date: Friday 19 February 2021 10.44am
To: Mike Campbell, Melissa Peters, Ben Townsend
Subject: Re: Re: Re: Re: Re: Brand integrity

Mike,

Why are you bringing us into this? I assumed we were only Cc'd because you felt your 'banana on wheels' comment deserved a wider audience.

I like the yellow chair. It adds a splash of Melissa's personality to an otherwise coherent space. I also like the bee and think we should all incorporate animated gifs into our emails. I couldn't think of any flying insects I identify with, but I did find one of Ben riding a cat.

David

....

From: Ben Townsend
Date: Friday 19 February 2021 10.47am
To: David Thorne
Subject: Re: Re: Re: Re: Re: Re: Brand integrity

Fuck you.

From: Melissa Peters
Date: Friday 19 February 2021 10.56am
To: David Thorne, Mike Campbell
Subject: Re: Re: Re: Re: Re: Re: Brand integrity

Thank you David but it doesnt matter now because Mike vandalized the chair. I can't return it because he wrote on it so that was smart. I cant even see if anyone else wants it because its ruined and I have marker on my dress which is ruined as well.

Sorry for thinking I could have a comfortable chair I guess or anything personal. I should have known better because I'm just the secretary.

Mel

....

From: Mike Campbell
Date: Friday 19 February 2021 11.13am
To: Melissa Peters, David Thorne
Subject: Re: Re: Re: Re: Re: Re: Brand integrity

Fuck off David. You do not like the chair. You said it looks like the kind people sit on to spin pots.

Melissa, cry me a river. Nobody said you can't personalize your area but there's a limit. You have a cactus on your desk that I hate but haven't said anything about. Or the phone holder shaped like a meditating frog. Furniture that compromises our brand is a completely different matter.

What client would trust us with their brand if ours isn't consistent? Perhaps you'd also like to swap the boardroom Aluminum Group chairs for bean bags? We can all sit around smoking bongs and listening to Pink Floyd.

I apologized for your dress and said I'd pay for a replacement. Use the company card. And remove the bee.

Mike

....

From: Melissa Peters
Date: Friday 19 February 2021 11.22am
To: Mike Campbell
Subject: Re: Re: Re: Re: Re: Re: Brand integrity

The dress is from Loft and they dont sell it anymore. I looked on the website. I wanted to wear it this weekend to a birthday party. I bought matching shoes.

Mel

From: Mike Campbell
Date: Friday 19 February 2021 11.27am
To: Melissa Peters
Subject: Re: Re: Re: Re: Re: Re: Re: Re: Brand integrity

Melissa,

If you're trying to make me feel bad it won't work. The damage to your dress is a consequence of your own actions. You should be thankful I even offered to pay for a replacement.

And the offer will be retracted immediately if I see that bee again.

Mike

....

From: Melissa Peters
Date: Friday 19 February 2021 11.30am
To: Mike Campbell
Subject: Re: Re: Re: Re: Re: Re: Re: Re: Re: Brand integrity

Can I get a dress and a pair of shoes?

Mel

From: Mike Campbell
Date: Friday 19 February 2021 11.38am
To: Melissa Peters, David Thorne
Subject: Re: Re: Re: Re: Re: Re: Re: Re: Re: Re: Brand integrity

Fine. You're milking it though. The yellow dress isn't all that. It makes you look like a giant lemon.

David, please swap the spare chair in Gary's office with Melissa's old one. The yellow chair can go in the dumpster. We have interviews today with Kate and thin hair lady and if that chair is still here when they come, I will lose it.

And Melissa, smile when Kate comes in, nobody wants to see that face.

Mike

....

From: David Thorne
Date: Friday 19 February 2021 11.47am
To: Mike Campbell
Subject: Gary isn't happy

Mike,

Gary wants it on record that he's sick of his office being used as a junk room and that he should have been a pilot. Should I offer him a boat as compensation?

David

From: Mike Campbell
Date: Friday 19 February 2021 11.59am
To: David Thorne
Subject: Re: Gary isn't happy

Yes, very amusing David. We all look forward to your clever quips. The first thing I'm going to have the new HR manager do is add a section to the employee agreement about no office additions that dilute the brand. That includes frog phone holders. Who uses a phone holder? Just put it flat on your desk like a normal person.

And I think I'm going to offer Kate the position. She dresses well and drives a white Volvo XC90. Thin hair lady looks like she catches the bus.

Mike

....

From: Melissa Peters
Date: Friday 19 February 2021 12.17pm
To: Mike Campbell, David Thorne
Subject: Re: Re: Re: Re: Re: Re: Re: Re: Re: Re: Re: Brand integrity

What face?

FEB 2021

20

SATURDAY

Seb has a girlfriend. He's all excited and in love and bought her a KitchenAide Artisan® Series 5 Quart Mixer. It was $70 off with his Best Buy staff discount. Seb had a girlfriend last year, a different one, but she wasn't very good. Apparently his new girlfriend, Hannah, is better than the old one, but the bar has been set pretty low. Hannah also works at Best Buy and I can only imagine what their conversations at work are like.

"Hannah, have you seen the new LG 5K display? It has a resolution of 218 pixels per inch. That's ultra-fine. Not as fine as you though, babe."
"Arigatō."

I used the Japanese word for thank you above because Hannah is Asian. She's not Japanese, she's Chinese, but nobody knows how to pronounce Xièxièň. Why is there an arrow above a letter? Hannah isn't even her real name, her real name is something unpronounceable that sounds a bit like a cat trying to say hello. We're all going out to dinner tonight, so Holly and I can meet her, and Seb told me not to say anything racist.

"Why would I say anything racist? I'm the least racist person on the planet."

"Please. When my friend Darnell told you he's been applying for jobs, you asked if he receives less callbacks because he has a black person's name."

"That's not being racist. I was implying there's racism in corporate America and was asking if it affected him."

"Darnell isn't a black person's name."

"Of course it is. It has an unexpected consonant. That's how black people come up with names for their kids; they add or swap a few superfluous consonants to normal names."

"Wow. Just don't say anything you think might be funny tonight. It won't be. It never is."

"Perhaps you should give me topics to avoid."

"Being good at maths, eating dogs, knowing Kung Fu, looking the same, communism, cheap manufacturing, and being short. Especially being short."

"Why? How tall is she?"

"4'3"."

"Are you serious? That's like the average height of a five-year-old. Is she a dwarf? Are her arms and legs in proportion or are they stumpy with sausage fingers?"

"She's not a dwarf. Please just don't make jokes about her height or say anything that could be construed as racist tonight. I like her a lot."

"Fine. I'll be on my best behaviour."

"Thank you."

"Does she have a normal shaped head or is perfectly round like a basketball?"

FEB 2021

21
SUNDAY

Illustration showing relative size difference between Seb (left) and Hannah.

Dinner last night went well. The waitress asked if we needed a booster seat for "the little one." It's understandable that some people have difficulty determining the age of Asians because they all look fifteen until they suddenly look eighty, but Hannah looks like a preschooler. Seb held her hand on the way in and to anyone else it probably looked like he was being a good big brother to his adopted sister. Hannah is nice enough though, and I managed to avoid mentioning her height or anything that might be construed as racist.

"What size shoe do you take, Hannah?"
"Dad."
"What? It's not a height question, it's a shoe size question. Small feet are a sign of beauty in some Asian cultures. Women bandage their feet so they don't grow. I saw that on a show about Geishas."

FEB 2021

22

MONDAY

We officially have two new employees at the agency. Mike offered Kate the HR position because she wears expensive shoes. She started today. Thin hair lady was a close second but her fifteen years of experience in the industry were overshadowed by the fact she drives a Hyundai. She was initially suspected of being a bus catcher, but apparently driving a Hyundai is worse.

"Have you ever even been in a Hyundai, Mike?"
"No, I'm not poor."
"It's the newer model at least."
"That's worse. It says, 'I just bought this Hyundai.'"

Our other new employee, Ashley, also started today. Her office space is next to Walter's and he's completely smitten. He's been making her coffees, giving her tips on which pens write best, and he swapped his keyboard with hers because his is less 'clackety'. I heard him tell her that she smelled like dryer sheets, "The scented ones, not the plain ones," and that he's a great dancer. A few minutes ago in the kitchen, he asked me if I think it would be weird if he wrote her a song.

"What type of song?"

"Just a song."

"I didn't know you play an instrument."

"I don't."

"Are you going to sing it to her? Please tell me you are."

"No, I'll email it to her. Maybe as a pdf."

"Nice. You should use the typeface OCR-B."

"The barcode font? No, I'll probably use Myriad Pro Semibold."

Update: 11.55am

Walter just asked me if I know a word that rhymes with 'meticulous'. He's going with 'frictionless' so I assume the song is about something clean and slippery.

Update: 12.45pm

Small bump on the road to love. Walter surprised Ashley with a Subway 6" Meatball Marinara Melt for lunch, but it turns out she's vegan. He was slightly crestfallen but covered it well by stating, "I don't really like meat either. Because I love animals and care about the world. They're just really good meatballs." He also stated that his favourite animal is the penguin because it mates for life.

Update: 1.05pm

Walter asked Ashley if she's ever been bitten by a parrot then peeled off a Band-Aid to show her his infected finger. She asked if it hurt and he said, "Only when I poke things."

Update: 1.25pm

Ben asked Ashley if she wanted to learn how to use the spiral binder so Walter's kind of pissed. He joined them in the stationery room and is critiquing Ben's poor choice of spiral size for the document thickness.

Update: 1.50pm

While Walter was downstairs, Jodie walked past Ashley's desk and said to her, "I think someone's got a little crush on you." Ben yelled from his office, "Oh my god, I was just showing her how to use the spiral binder. You're as bad as Walter."

Update: 2.05pm

I informed Walter of the rumour going around that Ben is planning to ask Ashley out. He's currently in Ben's office with the door closed, but the blinds are open. Ben is making a WTF? face as Walter waves a poster tube at him.

Update: 2.10pm

Mike ordered flowers for Kate's office. They're white lilies in a tall vase with a card that reads 'Have a great first week'. I replaced the card with one that says, 'I enjoyed showing you how to use the spiral binder' and moved the vase to Ashley's desk.

Update: 2.30pm

I'm being blamed for the flowers even though it's clearly not my handwriting on the card. I don't do my B's like that.

Update: 2.50pm

Walter just sent Ashley a friend request on Facebook. She didn't respond within thirty seconds so Walter asked if she'd seen his friend request. He also changed his profile photo to one of him at a fun run.

Update: 3.10pm

In what may be the oddest courting ritual I've ever witnessed, Walter is demonstrating to Ashley how 'staticy' the carpets are. It's like one of those wildlife documentaries where birds perform mating dances, but with quick shimmying then touching things.

Update: 4.00pm

Walter just proved to Ben he can do a headstand. There are scuff marks from his shoes on the wall next to Ashley's desk now. Apparently he can do a headstand without the use of a wall, but only if he's in a swimming pool.

Update: 4:17pm

Very little work has been done in the art department today. I could have worked from home but then I would have missed Walter and Ben arguing over who can do the best

Transformers transforming noise. Ben is just saying 'Bshooom' in a deep voice but I told Walter that Ben's impression is a lot better than his so Walter added body movements to turn it up a notch. Ashley said she hasn't seen the movie so can't judge.

Update: 5.05pm

Okay. In a rather surprising turn of events, Walter brought his A game and asked Ashley if she'd like to grab a drink with him after work. He tried to make it sound casual, like he'd just thought of it and he had plenty of other things to do if she was busy, but his face was bright red and you could see the panic in his eyes. He performed an odd little wobble of relief when she said yes.

They left together a few minutes ago and Walter grinned and did a little fist punch as he passed my office. On their way down the stairs, I heard him tell Ashley she looks like Selena Gomez from behind, "But less Mexican."

FEB 2021
23
TUESDAY

Apparently Walter and Ashley are a thing now. According to Walter, they didn't kiss, but they almost did, but then they didn't. I did hear him whispering something to Melissa downstairs and heard her reply, "You should definitely do that," so perhaps he's going to propose. That would make the day more interesting.

Not all days at the agency are exciting adventures. Some days, like today, consist of doing actual work. It's horrible. This morning, we had a group meeting in the boardroom to demonstrate to Ashley and Kate that it's possible to have a meeting at any moment for no reason at all. We covered Netflix shows, Mike's kitchen renovation, the price of toothpaste, and where all the pet hair is still coming from. We think it's in the air vents.

Kate wants a one-on-one chat with each of us at some point today. Probably just to get to know us a bit better and work out the lay of the land. I might pretend to be partially deaf and give her answers that have nothing to do with what she asks. Melissa and Jodie will no doubt see it as an opportunity to inform Kate just how hard done by they are by the other person and the difficulties they face in such a toxic work environment. I told Walter the one-on-ones are an established HR technique to gauge communication skills by seeing how long the staff member can hold direct eye contact.

Update: 1pm

Walter was just called to his meeting. I saw him practicing holding his eyes open as wide as he could as he went down the stairs. Ashley is at lunch so Melissa took the opportunity to fill us in on the gossip. Walter isn't going to propose, he's going to buy vinyl letter stickers and name his kayak Ashley.

Update: 1.20pm

Walter's eyes are bright red so he must have won the staring contest. Apparently they just chatted about his role and where he'd like to be in five years. He told Kate that he'd like to be the boss of the place and the winner of the Tour de France.

Update: 1.45pm

Melissa's meeting with Kate must have gone well. She came out wiping away tears and Kate gave her a hug. Jodie has her work cut out for her.

Update: 1.57pm

Gary's meeting was quick. It was held in his office rather than Kate's because he's 'nobody's bitch'.

Update: 2.15pm

Jason had his meeting. That's right, there's an employee at the agency named Jason. I never mention him because I don't like him and it annoys him that I never mention him. This is his only mention in my books and will be his last. Enjoy your six lines of inclusion, Jason. And brush your teeth. They look like half sucked jelly beans.

Update: 2.50pm

Rebecca's meeting was the longest so far. As production manager - in charge of coordinating project timelines - she probably has the best grasp of each employee's strengths and weaknesses. It's why I bought her a Starbucks Frappuccino while I was out at lunch and asked her what she did on the weekend. It was an excruciating five minutes so it had better be worth it. For those interested, Rebecca went for a jog with her friend Beth on Saturday and then did some washing. On Sunday, she made a pasta salad and watched a documentary about the Royal family.

Update: 3pm

Ashley's meeting was quicker than Gary's. She doesn't have any traumatic experiences to share yet and is still excited about being at the agency. It's like that scene in that movie where the guy who hasn't seen the ocean before walks into it with his arms spread wide in wonder. He's never stepped on a sharp shell or been stung by a jellyfish or had something touch his leg. I stood on a crab once. A big one.

Update: 3.20pm

Ben gave me the finger and smirked as he entered Kate's office. I took it as 'Ha, my meeting is before yours so I get to preempt anything bad you may say about me and let Kate know the truth in advance. Checkmate. You have been bettered today.'

Update: 3.40pm

Jodie took her portfolio into her meeting. I have no idea why. Walter is panicking a bit because he asked me if we were meant to show our portfolios and I acted shocked that he hadn't.

"Nobody told me."
"It was in the memo. You didn't get the memo?"
"No. What did it say?"
"That we have to bring our portfolio into the meeting. Failure to do so will be an immediate ten-point deduction from our HR score. Did you at least email Kate a photo of yourself like she asked?"

Update: 4.10pm

There wasn't much point to my meeting with Kate. I was in her first and second interview, and Mike and I went for a drink with her after offering the position. She did ask me what I thought the best and worst aspects about working at the agency were though. I told her money and having to do work as there's not much point lying to HR managers.

203

They've heard it all and know the key words. Sure, you can bullshit that working with a dedicated team of professionals is the best aspect and the lack of enough hours in a day to get everything done is the worst, but there's no magic HR points to collect.

"Sorry, Kate, I'm completely deaf in one ear and the other is full of wax. Did you just ask me if Ben has ever touched me inappropriately?"
"No, I asked if you find the F90-A forms helpful at all."
"Yes he has."

The F90-A form is something Jennifer, our previous HR manager, came up with. She introduced it a few weeks after her office suggestion box was scrapped. I thought the suggestion box was a great idea at first, as it allowed one to throw coworkers under a bus anonymously, but apparently anonymity only applies to other people around here.

The F90-A features the world's cringiest checklist, a bunch of faces showing various moods, and random inane fields such as 'Did you smile a lot this week?' and 'What was your favorite lunchtime meal?' Actually, I might scan one in as it's worth sharing. I've never filled one out correctly, not even once, and yet Jennifer made me complete one every single Friday.

F90-A

Date August 4th	Name David

Weekly Checklist

- [ ] I achieved a lot this week
- [ ] I felt valued
- [ ] I felt safe
- [ ] I felt welcome
- [ ] I felt included
- [ ] I felt part of a team
- [x] I felt something touch my leg

How did this week make you feel? ☹ ☹ 😐 🙂 😊 [x] Y

Did you smile a lot at work this week? [ ] Y [ ] N [x] Just when leaving

What was your favorite lunchtime meal? _Skittles_

What was your most satisfying moment? _Leaving_

Did you achieve everything you set out to achieve this week? [ ] Y [ ] N [x] other

What made you laugh this week? _Ben's car accident_

What made you frown? _The destruction of turtle habitats_

What could make next week better? _A mariachi band_

Did you make a coworker smile this week? [ ] Y [ ] N [x] Who cares?

Signature

Office Use Only

Ref: [x] F90-A [ ] F90-B	Lodged: [x] Y [ ] N
Followup [ ] Y [x] N	Date AUG / 0 6 / 2018

RECEIVED

205

FEB 2021
24
WEDNESDAY

I received my second shot of the Covid-19 vaccine this morning. According to reputable social media sources, the second shot included the activator for the magnetic tracking device I received with the first shot. I'm now a red blinking dot on government software that can pinpoint my location to within three feet.

"We have him."
"Good job. Location?"
"On the couch. He's watching television. Apparently it's a 4K documentary about lizards."
"Status?"
"Eating chips."

It's rather impressive they were able to fit a microchip - with a power source that can transmit a signal through muscle, fat and skin to a remote device - inside an injection. You'd think there'd be easier ways to track people, like through their phones, but what do I know? I'm not a microchip expert like Holly's mother Maria. She's also an expert on ballot machines and the mole people who live beneath us.

Update: 1.45pm

If I hadn't stopped to get Starbucks on my way to the office, I would have witnessed the catalyst of Ben and Gary's argument. It seems to be escalating well without my involvement though.

Usually, it's Melissa and Jodie who provide the *Battle Royale* type entertainment. They were both put on administrative leave last year after a discussion regarding boots and bob haircuts turned into an actual wrestling match. Jodie lost a chunk of hair, an Arco floor lamp and a projector were damaged, and Gary was elbowed in the throat when he tried to separate them. He had to lie on the floor of his office for several minutes but he does that a lot so there's no way of knowing if he was just milking it.

According to Rebecca, Gary and Ben's heated argument started when Ben put two large boxes of printer toner in Gary's office. That's the thing with arguments, they rarely start with something actually worth arguing over; I probably would have put the boxes in there as well. Gary has the largest office, but the smallest desk, so it's like he's sitting in a warehouse.

Gary is currently in the process of stacking archive boxes in Ben's office. He yelled, "Let's see how you like it!" and Ben yelled back, "Why are you even working here? You're old. Go fishing or something you old coot!"

Update: 1.53pm

I don't think I've heard anybody be called a coot before. For a second I thought he said cunt in a thick Scottish accent. Coot is hardly on the high end of the insult scale, but Gary wasn't overly impressed by it. He grabbed a scale model of *The Iron Giant* robot from Ben's desk and snapped the arms off. As a fellow collector of scale models, Gary should have known better. Ben stormed into Gary's office - looking for something personal of his to break - but Gary doesn't have any personal items, not even a photo, so Ben kicked over Gary's chair and a plastic plant instead. He also grabbed a big-button calculator off Gary's desk and tried to snap it, but it was too strong.

Update: 2.02pm

Kate is involved. She flew upstairs, four steps at a time, like a superhero rushing in to save the day. I knew there'd eventually be a situation where her HR skills would be put on display, but I assumed she'd be more astonished by our behaviour than excited.

She and Ben are currently in Ben's office with the door closed. My office shares a vent though so if I get on all fours and put my ear to it, I can hear everything being said. Ben stated that he outbid seventy people on eBay for the robot, and Kate asked if he couldn't glue the arms back on. Ben is, rightly so, outraged at this suggestion, and demanded Gary be disciplined and pay restitution.

Update: 2.05pm

It turns out the arms just snap back on. That's hardly the point though.

Update: 2.15pm

Kate invited Gary into Ben's office. I was expecting some kind of textbook HR conflict resolution speech, but Kate told Gary that "damaging something that meant a lot to Ben over fucking boxes was a dick move" and that he should apologise. Gary informed her that he wasn't going to apologise, because he's sick of his office being used as a storage room, and that the robot looked fine. Ben countered that the left arm is looser than it was and won't hold a pose.

Kate gave Gary the option of either apologising or having an F26-A formal complaint filed against him - to which Gary stated that he would apologise if, and only if, Ben first apologised for calling him an old coot. Ben said, "I'm sorry for calling you an old coot, Gary." and Gary replied, "Well, I'm not sorry I broke your stupid toy. Stay the fuck out of my office."

Update: 2.45pm

I'm glad Gary has a formal complaint against him. I don't feel so alone now. It's as if we're members of a gang. The bad boys of the agency. I told Gary this and he said he'd never be in a gang with me, because I'm a pussy, and that Ben is just lucky he didn't use karate against him. He also closed down his computer and left for the day. Ben has also left, citing stress from the unwarranted attack. I might leave shortly as well as my left arm is throbbing from the vaccine this morning which makes it difficult to type.

Update: 3.20pm

I haven't left yet as I'm supervising Walter. He was out all afternoon, at a press check, and missed the robot attack. I told him I need him to help move some stuff into Gary's office for me because I can't use my left arm. The photocopier and water cooler are already in there and he's currently dragging in a shelf of paper samples and poster tubes. There's also a box of computer cables, two boxes of Christmas decorations, and around forty archive boxes. Gary can still get to his desk, but he has a choice of two winding paths and one leads to a dead end.

From: Mike Campbell
Date: Thursday 25 February 2021 10.19am
To: David Thorne
Subject: AGC

David,

We have the AGC meeting this afternoon at 2. I'm going to go straight there from the airport so you'll have to make your own way there.

Mike

....

From: David Thorne
Date: Thursday 25 February 2021 10.23am
To: Mike Campbell
Subject: Re: AGC

Mike,

Not a problem. Why are you going to the airport?

David

From: Mike Campbell
Date: Thursday 25 February 2021 10.28am
To: David Thorne
Subject: Re: Re: AGC

Patrick is flying to Seattle. His sister is in the hospital with head cancer or something so he's going to see her.

I'll meet you outside AGC at 1.45.

Mike

....

From: David Thorne
Date: Thursday 25 February 2021 10.32am
To: Mike Campbell
Subject: Re: Re: Re: AGC

That works. Sorry to hear about Patrick's sister.

David

....

From: David Thorne
Date: Thursday 25 February 2021 10.37am
To: Mike Campbell
Subject: Re: Re: Re: Re: AGC

Don't be. She's a hateful bitch and I hope she dies.

Mike

From: Mike Campbell
Date: Friday 26 February 2021 3.04pm
To: David Thorne
Subject: Oh no

David,

Patrick's sister Ava died this morning and now I feel terrible for saying I hope she dies.

Mike

....

From: David Thorne
Date: Friday 26 February 2021 3.09pm
To: Mike Campbell
Subject: Re: Oh no

Yes, it was most likely that which caused it. You should have sent thoughts and prayers; it's the American version of Universal Healthcare.

David

From: Mike Campbell
Date: Friday 26 February 2021 3.14pm
To: David Thorne
Subject: Re: Re: Oh no

Patrick is staying in Seattle to organize the funeral. I'm flying there tomorrow to be with him. That means you will have to do the Glo_2O presentation in Phoenix Monday.

Mike

....

From: David Thorne
Date: Friday 26 February 2021 3.21pm
To: Mike Campbell
Subject: Re: Re: Re: Oh no

That's not much notice. I'd prefer to reschedule the meeting.

David

....

From: Mike Campbell
Date: Friday 26 February 2021 3.29pm
To: Mike Campbell
Subject: Re: Re: Re: Re: Oh no

No, the CEO is flying in for the meeting. It's too late to re-schedule. Take Gary or Ben if you want.

Mike

From: David Thorne
Date: Friday 26 February 2021 3.37pm
To: Mike Campbell
Subject: Re: Re: Re: Re: Re: Oh no

I'd rather fly alone to be honest. The last time I flew with Gary, he demanded the cabin temperature be raised, told a male flight attendant not to fuck with him because he knows karate, threatened to sue the airline for bumping his knee with a drink cart, and shouted at a child for crying.

Flying with Ben isn't any better. He played Microsoft's *Flight Simulator* at a friend's house once, so now he's an expert on ailerons, wind speed, and collision avoidance systems.

Holly mentioned she wanted to see Arizona a while back so I might see if she wants to go. I'll cover the extra ticket. I'll need a hire car and at least two nights there though. I'm not flying back straight after the presentation.

David

....

From: Mike Campbell
Date: Friday 26 February 2021 3.44pm
To: Mike Campbell
Subject: Re: Re: Re: Re: Re: Re: Oh no

I don't care what you do as long as the presentation goes well. I've got my own shit to deal with at the moment.

Mike

FEB 2021
27
SATURDAY

Holly likes travelling a lot more than I do. When I announced I had to fly to Phoenix and she could join me, it was like a video game character gaining a power-up. She was up until 3am last night working on our itinerary. Most people have a relatively flexible list of things to see and do when travelling, but Holly uses a pinboard with pieces of string like you see in shows about serial killers.

"Okay, we arrive in Phoenix Sunday at 1.15pm. Allowing 37 minutes to pick up the rental car, we should be checked in to the hotel by 2.18pm. You'll probably want to waste time by showering so I've allowed 22 minutes for that, but it still means we'll be out of the hotel by 2.45 - depending on how quick the elevators are - and at The Japanese Friendship Garden by 3.18pm. It closes at 4pm so we can't fuck around. I've booked a restaurant for 7.15pm so that gives us three hours and fifteen minutes for travel, photo ops, and shopping for a fridge magnet, a scarf, a Christmas tree ornament, and a carved dog figurine. Do you think your 10am presentation the next morning will take longer than 14 minutes?"

"Probably."

"Well that's very inconvenient."

FEB 2021

28

SUNDAY

Our flight was delayed so I'm not allowed to have a shower when we reach the hotel. Also, it's a five and a half hour flight from DC to Phoenix and I forgot to download any new music or movies, so I'm watching a show on the inflight entertainment about an old guy and his redheaded wife who buy a chateau in France and renovate it. I'm surprisingly into it and have learned a lot about installing a lift in a turret and moat maintenance.

Holly is currently asleep next me, softly snoring, as she had a late night deciding which thirty outfits to pack.

"Do you really need that much for two nights?"
"Of course I do, Phoenix is in a desert; I have to pack for two climates. Plus we might go swimming or out somewhere nice."
"We're not going swimming."
"You don't know that. Do you have room in your bag for these boots and my makeup case?"
"No, I'm only taking my laptop bag. There's just enough extra room in it for two extra shirts, two pair of socks and jocks, a tie, and my toiletries. I'll wear my suit on the plane."

"You can't be serious? You're not George Clooney. Are you going to wear a suit sightseeing and shopping?"

"Yes. People do shop in suits."

"We're driving to Sedona after your presentation. Are you going to wear your suit in Sedona?"

"What's in Sedona?"

"Big red rocks."

"I can look at big red rocks in a suit."

"What if we go hiking?"

"We're not going hiking."

"You don't know that."

Update:

With hindsight, wearing a suit on the plane probably wasn't the wisest choice. I wasn't overly comfortable and my feet must have swollen because my oxfords now feel too small. Also, rushing through the airports earlier with slippery leather soles meant doing the *Risky Business* slide at every turn. It was fun the first few times but you have to judge it well. Holly tried to convince me to buy a pair of sneakers from an airport shop, but there's no way I'm wearing sneakers with a suit. I get that it was a thing during the Eighties but so was acid-wash denim. The only positive thing that can be said about acid-wash denim is that it hid cum stains well.

"Wow, is that an acid-wash jeans and jacket ensemble?"

"No, I'm just completely covered in cum. Accident at the horse wanking farm."

218

Due to my swollen feet, I saw most of The Japanese Friendship Garden from a bench. If you've seen one carved rock pagoda you've seen them all though, and I have koi at home. Holly had some notion about walking the entire path together but I could see her head above the foliage whenever she crossed arched bridges. I waved the first couple of times but Holly didn't wave back so I didn't bother after that.

Holly got her fridge magnet, scarf, and Christmas tree ornament. I got blisters. We couldn't find a wooden carved dog figurine so Holly settled for one of a skinny horse. Apparently I'm going to be carrying all this stuff home through airports because I only have my laptop bag. The point of only taking a laptop bag was so I didn't have to carry anything else but that logic seems lost on Holly. Technically, she's a guest on this trip and, as such, should keep her impositions to a minimum.

Update:

There's no coffee maker in our hotel room so it's a 1-star rating on Tripadvisor from me I'm afraid. Also, the television has a huge bevel and doesn't have HGTV so I can't watch episodes of *Escape to the Chateau*. I'll have to wait until the flight back to find out how Dick's homemade pig smoker turned out.

MAR 2021
1
MONDAY

The presentation went well. It was a bit of a sell as everyone in the boardroom was well into their sixties, but after explaining what a music drop is they became quite enthusiastic about the tagline.

"So it's like that part of the song you played, what was it?"

"*Beautiful Now* by Zedd."

"Yes, where it 'dropped'. Drops in music are something most people in the 20 to 30 demographic would be familiar with?"

"Yes."

"And the 'drop' is a good thing?"

"Very much so."

"I do like the glowing bottles and the connection between the music drop and flavor drop. I'm not sure about the choice of music though, it was a bit annoying."

"Yes it was, we're not the target demographic though. That track was just an example, we wouldn't be able to afford the licensing rights. The production company we use can come up with something similar."

"Some of Billy Joel's songs have good 'drops'."

"They do?"

"Yes, many of them actually."

"Nice. It's not exactly the audience we're targeting though. Not too many dance venues have people dancing and waving about glow sticks to Billy Joel."

"I went to a Billy Joel concert at the Wells Fargo Center a few years back and people in the audience had glow sticks."

"They did?"

"Yes, a family a few rows down from us had them."

"Well, we can certainly look at Billy Joel tracks as an option. Again, the licensing might be a problem and glow sticks and water bottles are generally more synonymous with raves and DJs, but..."

"No, we'll go with your direction on this. I saw a few heads nodding along to the music and everyone smiled at the bottles lighting up part."

"So we have signoff on the tagline?"

"Yes, it's perfect. Let your team know we're excited about the direction."

"I will."

From: David Thorne
Date: Monday 1 March 2021 11.17am
To: Mike Campbell
Subject: Presentation

Mike,

Presentation went okay. They have a few changes though. Instead of dance music, they'd prefer Billy Joel's *Uptown Girl* and instead of a 'drop' they want Billy Joel smiling at the camera and giving the thumbs up.

Also, instead of *When the flavor drops*, we're going with *Ah, that's the taste of uptown, girl!*

Holly and I are driving to Sedona to look at big red rocks so I will be off email for the rest of the day. We can look at the changes when I'm back in the office Wednesday.

I hope Patrick is holding up and the funeral goes well.

David

....

"Mike is calling you. Do you want me to answer it?"
"No, let it go to voicemail. He knows I don't answer my phone while I'm driving."
"You have to take the next right to get onto I-17."
"Then what?"
"Then nothing. We stay on I-17 for 99 miles. I've allocated two five-minute bathroom stops, a thirty-minute break for lunch, and a ten-minute photo op next to a big cactus. Do you want a gummy bear?"
"Sure."
"What colour?"
"Are the yellow ones pineapple or banana?"
"They're lemon."
"Red then."
"You have a message from Mike. Do you want me to read it to you?"

"Yes, please."

"Okay, it says, 'Nice try but I've already spoken to Doug. He called me after the meeting. Well done. They're going to have us look at 2 more products. I'll have Melissa upgrade your return flights as a pat on the back.' Well that was nice of him."

"Yes, he can be nice occasionally."

"I'll keep a gummy bear each for the flight."

"Why would you keep a gummy bear for the flight?"

"They're marijuana gummies. There was a store near the building you had your meeting in. It's completely legal in Arizona, you don't even need to buy socks."

"Are you serious, Holly?"

"What?"

"Why didn't you tell me it was a marijuana gummy bear before I ate it? I have to drive for two hours on roads I've never been on before."

"Oh yeah."

"Wow. I'm not impressed at all."

"You'll be fine. They're not very strong. I had two while you were in the meeting and I don't feel anything. Oh my god!"

"What?"

"That cactus. It was gigantic. And extra green."

"I feel violated. This is how girls must feel after learning someone put Rohypnol in their drink."

"Oh please, don't exaggerate. Nobody wants to molest you. We should turn around and go back to that cactus. We're never going to find a better cactus than that to take a photo next to."

Update:

I had every intention of writing something sarcastic about Sedona - probably something about having seen big red rocks before - but I now have neither the inclination to be sarcastic nor the vocabulary or skill to describe how overwhelmingly beautiful Sedona is.

I wasn't expecting this and I'm kind of thrown. I feel changed somehow and the rest of this book might just be bad poetry about big red rocks and being one with the universe. There's apparently a bunch of spots in Sedona that have magic magnet powers, so perhaps I drove through one without realising it.

I *have* seen big red rocks before; there's a huge one in the middle of Australia called Ayers Rock - or *Uluru* in the Aboriginal language, which means 'big red rock'. My friend Bill and I climbed Uluru in 2005 when we were working on a tourism campaign for *Top Tourist Parks of Australia* and had to fly to Alice Springs.

Bill and I didn't climb all the way to the top, because it's pretty steep, but we got the point; it's a big red rock. It was pretty, I suppose, in a dry hot big red rock way, but I didn't feel a sense of wonder. Maybe because Uluru just looks like a lump of dough - regardless of whether you're ten miles from it or at standing at the base. It wasn't even that red, it was more of a grey. I read that you're not even allowed to climb it anymore, because it upsets the ghosts of dead

Aboriginals, so I don't see the point of visiting it all. Maybe if you're in the area. There's a resort in Alice Springs with a big pool shaped like a crocodile that's kind of cool. It doesn't look like a crocodile when you're sitting by it though, just from the air.

Maybe I'm just hard to impress. Bill liked Alice Springs a lot more than I did. Partly because a pool assistant named Cody let Bill suck him off inside the floatie shed. I had no idea at the time but I did wonder why it took them so long to pick out a big frosted donut.

"You couldn't decide, Bill?"
"About what?"
"The floatie. The shed's not that big. What were there, like ten floaties to choose from? Did you have to test them all out? Also, the two-hundred-dollar tip was a bit extravagant."
"It was worth every cent."
"You were only on it for five minutes."
"Best five minutes of the trip."
"Really? I might have a go then... no, too late, that kid is on it now."

Holly cried as we approached Sedona. Crying isn't an unusual event for her, she once cried during an advertisement for hearing aids, but I've only seen her cry over locations twice before; once when she first saw the Eiffel tower and once when the ball dropped in Times Square. I don't think I've ever cried over a location, I'm more of a, "Well this is nice," kind of person. It has to be a pretty special location for me to even get that emotional. I usually hate everywhere and can't wait to leave.

A few miles from our hotel, I pulled the car over and Holly I stood, holding hands on the side of the road like two lost halfwits, our brains attempting to process what we were seeing and failing. We may have stood there for ten minutes or twenty or just one.

"Well this is nice."

I'm no travel writer, so I won't even attempt to describe the view, but I did write a review on Tripadvisor about the pizza we had later that night. I wrote, "Best margherita pizza I've ever had." - which is a pretty big statement because I've had some really good ones. After further consideration, I realised someone reading the review might think I haven't had many or was exaggerating, so I added "I've had lots and I'm not exaggerating." Good writing is about detail. And commas and nouns.

"Right, we're moving here to live, Holly."
"Ha. It is beautiful."
"I'm not joking. We should sell everything and move here immediately. Why are we living in Virginia? It's a shithole compared to this place."
"We both have jobs and my parents live there."
"We'll quit our jobs and open a pottery shop. Kilns aren't

that expensive. We'll say the pots are made by local Indian tribes and make millions. Your parents can fly here to visit."

"My mom hates flying."

"She can catch a bus. Or stay home. This isn't a place for her bullshit anyway. We can visit them. Every five years or so. Or you can, I don't really need to go."

"And what if we eventually got bored of the big red rocks?"

"I don't think that's possible. Besides, it's not just the rocks, it's everything. Was that not the best pizza you've ever had in your life?"

"It was extraordinarily good."

"That's because it had magic magnet powers. It gets into everything here. That cut I had on my leg from the open dishwasher door? Completely healed. I saw it close up and disappear."

"That's not true."

"No, I think just leaving the bandaid off helped it dry out. Still, there's something almost tangible about the energy in this place. I'm serious about moving here."

"It could be our retirement plan."

"I'll be too old to climb the rocks then. See that big rock next to the one that looks like a boot? We should climb that tomorrow."

"You're going to climb a rock in a suit?"

"It doesn't look that steep."

"What about your feet?"

"They're all better. Magic magnet powers."

MAR   **2021**

2

TUESDAY

The rock was a lot steeper than it looked from our hotel balcony. Still, the early morning climb was worth it for the most part. Apparently it's quite a popular rock as there were about a hundred other people who had the same idea. Most were wearing shorts, caps and sneakers and some smartarse asked if I'd got lost on my way to a meeting. He had a backpack with a hose to drink out of, so he was one of those people. You know the type. I had a bottle of Fanta.

I sometimes experience social anxiety, and often feel self-conscious about what I'm wearing, but I was full of magic magnet powers this morning and didn't give a fuck. If anything, I felt more appropriately dressed than the other climbers. I wasn't trying to adapt to the environment, there was no prepwork, allowances, or caution. Just contrast. My slippery leather soles didn't detract from the experience, they emphasized it. I wish I'd worn a tie.

Also, I had the pool spider dream last night. The surface wasn't black though; it was rippled orange and red. I swam upwards, surfaced unimpeded, and was surrounded by big red rocks. It was sunny and Holly was playing a pan flute.

Update:

Our upgraded seats are nice. There are free microwaved hand towels. It's the first time Holly has flown first class and she's milking it for all it's worth; there's no button pushing for Holly, she does a little queen wave to summon the flight assistant whenever her glass of Rosé is empty.

"You don't want a neck pillow, David? Nikki will bring me another. They're complimentary."

"No, I don't like them. They look like little toilet seats."

"They're quite nice actually. Here, try mine."

"No, I'm fine. My neck isn't the kind that requires special support during plane rides."

"Just try it. You might be like, 'Oh my god, this is fantastic, why haven't I been using a neck pillow all this time?'"

"Yes, and then I'll become one of those people who wears neck pillows. It's all downhill from there. Next I'll be packing little sandwich bags of nibbles to eat on the plane."

"Well don't complain to me when we get to DC and you have a crick."

We have Wi-Fi on this flight and I've spent the last couple of hours looking up properties for sale in Sedona. The prices are kind of ridiculous and if Holly and I intend to move there, either my Shiba Inu needs to take off or we're looking at a tent on a vacant lot.

Update:

Dick's homemade pig roaster turned out well.

MAR 2021
3
WEDNESDAY

I have no idea what happened in the office while I was away but Melissa and Jodie are besties now. They went out for a long lunch together today and returned wearing matching cowboy boots. Where do you even buy cowboy boots in D.C.? I've only seen one cowboy around here and he's an old black guy who rides a bicycle with a trailer on the back and hangs out at Walmart. I walked past him once and he tipped his hat. I can't remember what I went to Walmart for, maybe tennis balls.

I guess Jodie is now attending Melissa and Andrew's wedding, which is a good thing I suppose, but I was looking forward to making up lies about the event to tell her later.

"Yes, I thought the cake was suspiciously large. It made sense when Miley Cyrus burst out of it and sang *Malibu* though. Best wedding ever. What did you do Saturday?"

Maybe I'm the bad energy in the office and everyone gets along perfectly when I'm not around. In which case I should try to be here more often. Factions form when you're not paying attention and nothing good comes of factions.

MAR 2021

4

THURSDAY

Holly ordered me a cowboy hat on Amazon. It's mustard coloured with a brown leather strap. If I do ever wear a cowboy hat, it's not going to be a mustard one. I told Holly to return it and we had a bit of an argument about social expectations and hat hair. I'm not a hat person. Some people can put on and take off hats all day long because they have the hair for it or maybe the right shaped head. For me, putting on a hat is a commitment. Once it's on, it's staying on. I don't have the kind of hair you can ruffle after taking off a hat; it goes flat and I look like one of those mental institution patients who wear their pants really high and masturbates constantly.

On the odd occasion when I wear a cap, perhaps camping or on a boat, I always make sure I have two additional caps in case I lose the first cap. The third cap is the second cap's backup, but if I lose the second cap, it's time to go home. I should probably have three spare caps but that's a lot of caps to be lugging about. Ideally, they'd have an elastic strap that goes under your chin to decrease the risk of being lost, especially in strong winds.

"Will I have to take my cowboy hat off for any reason?"

"Maybe during the ceremony."

"Well there you go, I'm not sitting through the ceremony with hat hair, so I'm not wearing it."

"Nobody is going to be looking at your hair during the ceremony. They're going to be looking at Melissa and Andrew."

"They might glance around. That's what I do. Nobody likes speeches. What I need is a little hat for under the cowboy hat. Like a fez."

Holly also ordered me something called a Bolo tie. It's essentially a neck shoelace with a metal clasp. I'm not wearing that either. I've seen the type of people who wear them - usually to blues festivals or somewhere similarly awful - and they look like idiots. I have no idea who came up with the concept, or whether it's just for decoration or functional in some way.

"Is that a shoelace around your neck?"

"Yes, it's a convenient way to carry a spare."

"But you're wearing boots."

'It's handy for other things. Like rappelling down very small cliffs or hog-tying a child."

"And why do you have a sock taped to your forehead?"

"Where do you keep your spare sock?"

"I don't carry a spare sock."

"Wow. Okay. Good luck with that if you step in a puddle or lose one in a strong wind."

MAR   2021
5
FRIDAY

Melissa is out today. I guess to do wedding stuff like getting a haircut before tomorrow. Her out of office reply sates that she will back in two weeks 'manned and tanned' which is an odd phrase. Wed and red wouldn't have been quite as 'ewy'. Actually, that's worse now that I think about it.

Mike told Melissa to change her out of office reply before she left yesterday, but because she ignored him, he's enlisted Walter to hack into her computer. They started on Melissa's Facebook page - in a cross-referencing attempt to discover her mother's maiden name - but quickly became sidetracked and are now scoring Melissa's friends out of ten. Apparently it's not misogynistic if you're gay; it's critiquing.

Gary is also out of the office today. He's had two Amazon parcels stolen from his front porch over the last week, so he's spending the day hiding in a bush. I told him he should buy one of those Ring doorbell systems, so he can keep an eye on his porch from anywhere, but he doesn't want the government knowing when he leaves the house. That's when they hide microphones under your coffee table.

Ashley is working on the packaging for a range of hair styling products and is quickly discovering that when Ben states he will, "Have the copy to you by tomorrow," it means he will start working on it next week, possibly Thursday, if everyone leaves him the fuck alone. Copywriters don't care about deadlines... No, actually, they don't care about *other people's* deadlines. They like having copy deadlines because it gives them a set amount of time not to do it until the last day. I walked into Ben's office earlier, to show him a video I took of Walter teaching Ashley dance moves, and he was watching the movie *Wonder Woman 1984* with the lights off.

"How is this research?"

"The product packaging I'm writing copy for incorporates an Eighties color palette. I'm watching this for the pop-culture references."

"Really, Ben?"

"Yes. Also, watch this... hang on, I'll rewind it a bit... there, did you see that?"

"See what?"

"When Wonder Woman jumped over the truck. Her dress lifted up and you could see her underwear."

Also, Rebecca and Jodie trapped me in the kitchen to inform me Walter and Ashley kissed in the stationery room while I was away. Apparently Walter told Gary who told Melissa who told her new bestie Jodie who told Rebecca. It's a secret so I had to promise not to tell Mike.

I wasn't looking forward to being back at work but it's bearable when it's like this - when it's a Friday and everyone has their own thing going on, and people are away so you can talk about them. According to Walter, Gary wears adult diapers and Melissa picks her nose and wipes it under her desk. He took a photo to support the accusation and it looked like a cave with stalactites.

"It's like seven years of snot. Do you want to know how I discovered it?"

"Sure, why not?"

"I tried to tape a USB cable to the underside of her desk and it wouldn't stick so I got under to have a look and I rubbed it, because I didn't know what it was, and some flakes fell in my mouth. They were salty."

"That's disgusting. When was this?"

"When you were in Arizona. Lots happened while you were away."

"Like what?"

"Ashley and I kissed."

"You did?"

"Yes, in the stationery room. So we're boyfriend and girlfriend now. We're trying to keep a secret though so don't tell anyone."

"Was this before or after Melissa's snot flakes went in your mouth?"

"After but I drank a Coke inbetween."

MAR 2021
6
SATURDAY

We were late to Melissa and Andrew's wedding because Holly has terrible navigation skills. Her total inability to plot and execute any trip is exacerbated by the fact she thinks she's a modern-day Magellan.

"It's your next left."

"Are you sure, Holly?"

"Yes. The North Star is currently 4.8 degrees below the meridian with a slight Equatorial bias."

"That's not the North Star, it's a plane."

"Your next right then."

Because Holly firmly believes she's gifted with some kind of built-in navigation system, like a bee or homing pigeon, she doesn't need to use Google Maps. Apparently robots don't know the quickest route because 'they're not the ones driving; they live on a server and have other stuff to do, like showing people where websites are.'

We visited the Grand Canyon by accident when we were in Arizona. It was a four-hour detour from where we were headed.

When I hear the word 'barn', I think of a rickety wooden structure, painted red, with a second level inside where the hay is kept. That second level is where the farmer's daughter and her lover copulate or where someone hides from a serial killer. Also, there's usually a pitchfork and maybe some chickens.

The barn that Melissa and Andrew were married in today wasn't rickety or red. It was white and more of an event venue shaped like a barn than an actual barn. It did have a second level but there wasn't any hay up there, just bathrooms and a bride's lounge. I'm not sure what a bride's lounge is but I assume it's where the bride gets changed and has last minute doubts and her mother or a fat friend says, "That's just the jitter's talking, he's a fine man."

Downstairs had several hay bales, but they were just for decoration. There were no pitchforks or chickens but there was a full-sized horse prop in the photo area. I think it was a stuffed horse because it looked real. Probably reinforced because Jodie and Rebecca sat on it for a photo without any issues.

I wore my suit to the wedding. I've been wearing it a lot lately - to work obviously, but also around the house, to the supermarket, and blowing leaves.

I did wear my cowboy hat though; it took me about four hours last night to colour it in black with a Sharpie. I actually went through four sharpies as the felt really sucked in the ink. Even the four wasn't enough and I had to cut open all the sharpies with a knife to use the fluffy inside bit. There are a few areas where the mustard colour still shows through, mostly under the brim because I did the bottom last. I considered spray painting it black, but I only had gloss. I didn't wear the neck shoelace, but I did wear a tie with little wagon wheel patterns on it. Technically they're boat steering wheels but you can't tell from a distance.

"Why are you wearing a boat tie, David?"
"Why are you wearing a plastic vest with tassels, Walter?"
"It's a cowboy vest."
"It's clearly part of a children's Halloween costume."
"No it isn't. It said adult on the bag."

Holly wore a blue floral dress with cowboy boots. The whole cowboy boots with a dress look is practically the only country thing that doesn't annoy me. It conjures visions of running your hand along wheat shafts and kissing horses on the nose. Also, drinking out of a hose for some reason.

If I ever write a romance novel, the female component is going to be a country girl who wears cowboy boots and floral dresses. I'll name her Cadence and she'll be in a wheelchair because of a horse-riding accident. The male component will be a good-looking but slightly eccentric inventor named Jackson. In the end, he'll make Cadence some kind of robot suit so she can ride again.

"Who are you messaging?"

"I'm not messaging anyone, Holly. I'm making notes."

"You're meant to be socialising. What are you making notes about?"

"My idea for a romance novel."

"Really?"

"Yes, it's about a country girl who's in a wheelchair because she fell off a horse. She's still hot though, and a good-looking inventor likes her so he builds her a robot suit."

"A robot suit?"

"Yes, so she can ride her horse again."

"Wouldn't she be too heavy to ride a horse if she's wearing a robot suit?"

"I haven't worked out all the details yet, just the premise and their names. I'll probably set it in Montana."

"If the girl is in a wheelchair, she could probably still ride a horse. The inventor could just add straps to a saddle. Is the girl a paraplegic or can she use her arms?"

"This is why I don't let you read my books until I've finished writing them. You ask too many questions and I become disillusioned with the whole thing."

"What are their names?"

"It doesn't matter now; they no longer exist. My romance novel is going to be about a female concert pianist who loses a hand in an elevator accident instead."

"Is her love interest going to build her a robot hand?"

"No, Holly, he also only has one hand and he learns to play the piano so they can play her favourite song together."

"Are they missing the same hand or opposite hands?"

The worst part about weddings is standing in a group trying to think of something to talk about. It's like being at someone's house but they have no chairs so you all have to stand facing each other for an hour or two. It's worse when the group consists mainly of people you spent several hours with at work the day before. Nobody stands in a group at work talking to each other, it would be weird. Usually, the conversations at work are the kind you have while you're doing something, or are on your way to do something. Without the doing something bit, the talking is the something. There's no escape. You can't say, "Right, well I'd better get back to it," if your doing it. Thankfully, as a smoker, "Right, I'm going outside for a cigarette," works in most environments. Not space or if you're on trial though.*

Mike and Patrick arrived while I was outside having a cigarette. Patrick went whole hog and his outfit included chaps and spurs. He has time for that kind of thing because he doesn't have to work. His parents invested in Google when it was just a startup and, after they died in a canal boat accident while on holiday in Copenhagen, Patrick and his sister inherited a lot of money. It was enough for Patrick to buy several properties all over the United States and rent

---

* *Seb added the 'not space or if you're on trial' bit while he was proofreading this book. He also stated, "There's hundreds of places it wouldn't work. Like in a submarine or plane or even a bus. Sure, you could get off the bus to have a cigarette, but it's not going to wait for you. You'll have to catch the next one."*

them out as Airbnbs. He also owns a whole bitcoin and a Tesla. It's very annoying.

"How are you, Patrick? Sorry to hear about your sister."
"At least someone is. Mike's glad she's dead."
"No, I'm not."
"How was the funeral?"
"Small. Ava didn't have any friends. Just cats. We had them put down."
"You put down her cats?"
"They were old, nobody would have wanted them. Also, Ava was cremated so I had a tattooist mix some of her ashes with ink and I got this frog tattoo on my wrist."
"Nice. Were frogs special in some way to Ava?"
"No, I just like frogs."
"Did Ava like frogs?"
"Everybody likes frogs. How was Sedona?"
"Indescribable."
'Yes, I love it there. I own an Airbnb overlooking Cathedral Rock."
"Of course you do."

Jealousy is built in to all of us. It's a genetic thing going back to when we were monkeys and someone had a bigger banana. Besides, it's a lot easier to blame the genetic thing for faults than to work on them. I'm less inclined to be jealous of others than I was just ten years ago though, so maybe it's not really a genetic thing at all, maybe it's a maturity thing. Or maybe my priorities have just changed.

Sometimes priorities change gradually - so gradually you might not even notice they've changed. Sometimes it can be an event that shunts a change of priorities. Like a heart attack, or losing a loved one, or visiting somewhere indescribable. It can't be just an age thing. I know a guy in his fifties whose priorities are Rolex watches and Porches - to divert attention from the fact he's short, unattractive, and uninteresting - and a guy the same age who sold everything and moved to Norway to study shrews after his wife and daughter died in a car accident.

Regardless, when you're told the path to success is to work hard and save for the things that are important to you and then you read about people raking it in because their cat looks grumpy or their weird kid yodeled in Walmart, it's difficult not to feel a twinge of jealousy.

"Seb, I have no definable talent to monetize so I'm going to need you to yodel in Walmart."

"That's not happening."

"Fine. I'll record you taking a bath and sell jars of the bathwater instead."

"That's not happening either."

"Mozart wrote his first symphony while he was still in the womb. How old are you now? Like seventeen?"

"Twenty-two."

"And how many symphonies have you written?"

"None."

"Get in the bath."

Also, after writing the bit about the weird kid who yodeled in Walmart, I Googled him (to check my memory wasn't playing tricks on me and he didn't actually juggle or do the robot) and I discovered he joined Billy Ray Cyrus on stage at a concert to sing *Old Town Road*. There's a video of it on YouTube and it's worth having a look at just so that when I state the kid is completely talentless, you can nod and say, "Yes, it's actually shocking how completely talentless he is. Also, how high were his pants? They're like two-thirds of his body. He should have just left it at the Walmart video."

That's not jealousy, I have no desire to be on stage with Billy Ray Cyrus. It didn't even look like the kid wanted to be there. Also, there's a moment in the video where Billy tells the crowd to sing along and nobody does. It's the best bit.

I left my hat on during Melissa and Andrew's nuptials. I'd actually worked out how to style my hair so I could take the hat off, but I didn't because the Sharpie rubbed off onto the top of my ears and forehead. I tried washing it off with soap in the bathroom, and Patrick tried hand sanitizer, but it didn't remove the stain and made the skin around it red. I actually considered leaving, that's how bad it was. I had to push my hat down further, to hide the line and redness, which left another line. Jodie took a group photo that shows my cowboy hat below my eyebrows with my ears folded at ninety degrees. She posted it on Facebook and tagged me so I untagged myself and unfriended her. I also reported the image.

Melissa looked nice, she wore a simple white dress with cowboy boots and some kind of flower wreath on her head. Andrew wore his Scout Leader uniform which makes no sense. Maybe he didn't get the memo about the country theme. Also, his vowels went on for about twenty minutes too long. I get that it was probably an important moment for him but I don't care if he'd stand between Melissa and an angry bear on a hiking path. Holly cried and said his speech was sweet though, so what do I know?

"Would you stand between me and an angry bear on a hiking path?"
"No, I assume we'd both be running."
"You're not meant to run from bears, their chase instinct kicks in. You're meant to stand your ground."
"I don't care what I'm meant to do, if there's an angry bear coming at me, I'm running. You can stand your ground if you want, it will give me time to climb a tree."

I threw Seb at an angry chicken once.

So, Melissa is a married woman now. She'll need new business cards since she's changing her last name. She's not Melissa Peters anymore, she's Melissa Woodcock - which I find far more hilarious than it probably is. Maybe that's why women care more about weddings than guys do; because the name change symbolises a new beginning as a different person with a different name. Guys don't get a new identity; they just get the wife and have to be in a lot of photos.

It's probably also why women usually organise the weddings. Guys would just have a barbecue with a few mates over. Maybe a bit of backyard cricket.

"Congratulations, Barry. Very nice."
"Thanks. I got it at Lowes. 25% off with a coupon. It has a smoker."
"No, I meant being married. Where are you going for your honeymoon?"
"I don't know, maybe the lake if the weather's nice next weekend."

I'm generalising of course. Mike and Patrick's wedding was a huge affair and we all had to fly to Acapulco for it. There was a monsoon during the ceremony and someone was stabbed by a flying umbrella.

The food was surprisingly good. With Melissa's country theme, I was expecting chicken in a basket and a pickle, but the caterers went with a Tex-Mex menu. With everyone from the agency plus assorted partners eating and passing drinks over our table, it was like that painting of Jesus and his friends. Usually, it would be Mike that played the part of Jesus, as he likes to be the centre of attention, but Gary had downed several tequila shots and treated everyone to a detailed recounting of his ingrown chest-hair wound. It was a story of triumph over adversary and included the chapters *It stuck to my sheets* and *Some of the stitches ripped when I reached up to change a light bulb.*

Rebecca and Jodie were each other's dates. Which is sweet but sad. More sad than sweet really. Both were fawning over Kate's husband, Dean, who looks like he's straight off the cover of *GQ* . Apparently Dean is an investment broker but when I told him I own a billion Shiba Inu he wasn't impressed. Kate's okay though, I quite like her so far. When she introduced me to Dean she said, "And this is David, he disguises apathy with humor." which I'm fairly certain was a compliment but if it wasn't, like I give a fuck.

Ben had a date but I have my suspicions he paid her to be there. I've never heard him mention a Denise before and she was at least twenty years his senior. Also, she stole the salt and pepper shakers off the table; I saw her put them in her bag. They weren't even that nice.

'Lost your date, Ben?"

"No she's just gone to powder her nose."

"I saw her get into an Uber while I was outside having a cigarette."

"Really? What a fucking bitch."

"Did she bring a lamp with her?"

"Why would she bring a lamp to a wedding?"

"She had one when she left. You can do a lot better."

"You think so?"

"No, I'm just being nice. That bridesmaid over there keeps checking you out though. The one shotgunning a mango White Claw. You should ask her to dance."

"I might actually... wait, where's my wallet?"

Walter wasn't lying about being a good dancer. I think he honestly believes it. He and Ashley looked like they were having fun and had discarded all efforts to hide their office romance. I asked Walter if he was happy and he said, "More than I've ever been," so that's nice.

I have no statistics on office romances but most of the ones I've witnessed have quickly become dumpster fires. Early in my career, while working as an interface designer for an Australian software engineering company called Lakewood, the marketing manager, Helen, had an affair with the CEO. I don't know how Helen's husband found out about the affair and I didn't see the attack - I was at a client meeting when it occurred - but I saw the aftermath; the shape of the blood splatter across the beige vertical blinds in the CEO's office is ingrained in my mind even to this day. It looked like a dandelion being blown. You can do a lot of damage with a claw hammer. The CEO didn't die immediately; he managed to walk out of his office and halfway down the corridor with the hammer imbedded in the side of his skull. At some point he must have attempted to remove it or touched the wound because there were scarlet handprints along the walls. I was once hit by a golf ball in the side of the head and I thought I was going to die, so I can't imagine what being hit with a hammer feels like. The husband simply walked out and drove himself to the police station. He was eventually sentenced to 12 years in prison, which doesn't seem a lot, but crimes of passion aren't usually premeditated. This happened in the Nineties so he's probably out by now...

No, I just Googled him, he died in prison from pancreatic cancer. Not a lot of comedy in the last few paragraphs of this book.

I'd met Helen's husband, and their kids, at a couple of company events. He was a good-looking guy, fit, I think he worked in construction. This was well before Facebook existed but I knew they owned a large house with a swimming pool from photos pinned to Helen's office corkboard. Everyone in the photos looked happy but you never really know what's going on behind closed doors, who the people are behind the presentation. They could be lizard people. At the time though, all I could think was, "Was it worth it?" For any of them. Mainly the husband though, because Helen was fat.

Holly made me line dance. It was more fun than I thought it would be, but not by much. I'm not a fan of dancing *or* group activities, so putting them together doesn't make it twice as fun, it makes it four times as avoidable. Maths. Technically, line dancing isn't really dancing though, its group stepping and spinning with an odd clap here and there. Maybe a little head tilt to indicate which way you're stepping or spinning. At least it's not just random arm and leg movements I suppose, the rules make it more of a sequence of actions. Line dancing is dancing in the same way that playing Guitar Hero is playing a guitar. It's just a pity about the shit music. There should be EDM line dancing.

There was a point in the evening, while I was sitting down to rest, that I looked around at the others dancing and enjoying themselves and thought, "I don't hate anyone here." Maybe it's not quite, "I like everyone here," but it's close. Holly smiled and waved, clapped and did a turn. She turned the wrong way and headbutted Jodie. Mike and Patrick were having photos taken on the stuffed horse; they were facing the horses rump, drunk and laughing. Gary was asleep, his head resting on a table beside dozens of empty shot glasses. Walter and Ashley were at the other end of the table - Ashley had her head on Walter's chest and he was stroking her hair. He grinned at me and I grinned back. Ben and the bridesmaid he'd asked to dance were kissing on a bale of hay. It was sloppy and disturbing and like they were having a contest to see who could kiss with their mouth the most open. Rebecca was drunkenly trying to explain something to Kate's husband. The explanation clearly required a lot of touching his chest. Kate, who was standing by her husband's side, looked at me, smiled and shook her head as if to say, "Some people, hey?"

Melissa and Andrew were doing the rounds and, when they reached our table, Melissa gave me a big hug and thanked me for buying them the Breville Bambino Plus Espresso Machine. Holly had decided Melissa deserved it for the amount of crap she puts up with from me. It was the first time Melissa and I have ever hugged but it didn't feel weird. Andrew told me to call him Andy but that's not going to happen.

"You missed the turn. You'll have to do a left up here and then two rights and, no, you missed the first left."

"You're a terrible navigator, Holly."

"I'm an excellent navigator. You're just terrible at following instructions. I have no idea how you manage to find your way around when you're driving alone."

"I use Google Maps."

"Then do that."

"I'm not pulling over to put our destination into Google Maps now. You should have informed me prior to leaving that you had no intention of taking your navigational duties seriously. If this were a ship, you'd be responsible for the deaths of everybody on board when we hit a reef. There'd be an inquiry."

"Good. Melissa is pregnant by the way."

"What? No she isn't."

"Yes she is. Five months. She told me they conceived in a tent."

"That seems appropriate somehow."

"Your new coworkers seem nice."

"Yes, I think they're going to work out well. It feels like we have a cohesive team again. I'm going to miss them when we move to Sedona."

"Really?

"No. I'll be too busy."

"Doing what?"

"Looking at big red rocks."

"Hmm. Just so you know, Sedona wasn't that great. You were just off your face."

MAR 2021

7

SUNDAY

Then I did magic and won.

About the Author

David Thorne was born in the Portuguese town of Sabrosa. His father was a minor member of Portuguese nobility and mayor of the town.

At the age of 25, Thorne enlisted in the navy and was given his own ship. After a quarrel with the King of Portugal, who denied Thorne's persistent requests to lead an expedition to reach the Spice Islands from the east, Thorne left for Spain where he devoted himself to studying the latest shipping charts and maps.

After having his proposed expeditions to the Spice Islands repeatedly rejected by the king of Portugal, Thorne renounced his Portuguese nationality and turned to the King of Spain for funding. Thorne proposed reaching the Spice Islands by a western route, a feat which had never been accomplished. Hoping this would yield a commercially useful trade route for Spain, the king approved the expedition.

Thorne's fleet consisted of five ships, carrying supplies for 270 men. They sailed west across the Atlantic toward South America, making landfall at Rio de Janeiro. From there, they sailed south along the coast, searching for a way through or around the continent. After three months of searching, weather conditions forced the fleet to stop their search to wait out the winter. They found a sheltered natural harbor at the port of Saint Julian, and remained there for five months. During the winter, one of the fleet's ships, the Santiago, was lost in a storm.

Following the winter, the fleet resumed their search for a passage to the Pacific. While exploring the area, one of the remaining four ships deserted the fleet, returning east to Spain. A week later, Thorne found a bay which eventually led the fleet to a strait which allowed them passage through to the Pacific.

Based on the incomplete understanding of world geography at the time, Thorne expected a short journey from the passage to Asia, perhaps as little as three or four days.

The Pacific crossing took three months and twenty days. The long journey exhausted their supply of food and water and thirty men died, mostly of scurvy. Thorne himself remained healthy, mainly because of his personal supply of preserved quince.

Eventually the fleet reached the island of Samar in the eastern Philippine Islands. They weighed anchor and remained there for a week while the sick crew members recuperated. Thorne converted the locals to Christianity and after resupplying, sailed on to the next island.

After successfully converting several more tribes to Christianity, they reached the island of Mactan. Most islands had accepted Christianity readily, but the island of Mactan resisted.

Thorne and members of his crew attempted to convert the Mactan natives by force, but in the ensuing battle, Thorne was struck by a bamboo spear, then surrounded, and finished off with machetes.

By the Same Author

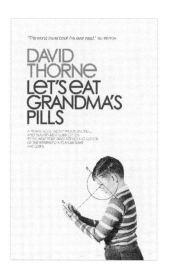

DAVID THORNE
THAT'S NOT HOW YOU WASH A SQUIRREL

A BOOK ABOUT TOWERED SANDCASTLES, SOCIOGRAPHY, AND SECRET UNDERGROUND TUNNELS. BY THE NEW YORK TIMES BESTSELLING AUTHOR OF *THE INTERNET IS A PLAYGROUND* AND *27BV6*.

DAVID THORNE
LOOK EVELYN, DUCK DYNASTY WIPER BLADES. WE SHOULD GET THEM.

A BOOK ABOUT DEATH AGENCIES, ABOVE GROUND POOLS, AND MAGNETISM. BY THE NEW YORK TIMES BESTSELLING AUTHOR OF *THE INTERNET IS A PLAYGROUND* AND *27BV6*.

DAVID THORNE
THE INTERNET IS A PLAYGROUND

INTERNATIONAL EDITION

A NEW YORK TIMES BESTSELLING BOOK ABOUT OVERDUE ACCOUNTS, MISSING CATS, PIE CHARTS, EASTER PLAYS, PARTY INVITES, AND ALLIGATORS. BY THE AUTHOR OF *27BV6*.

Printed in Great Britain
by Amazon

35506602R00155